Table of Contents

Philosophy and Structure

Program Objectives

Why Study Science? Science has taken its place beside language development and mathematics as one of the necessary foundations of education. Increasingly, young people need an understanding of basic scientific concepts and methods in order to assess the scientific issues that will shape their lives. It is equally important for students to have a solid grounding in the concepts and process skills used in scientific inquiry so that they will be better able to solve problems encountered in other areas of study and in dealings with the everyday world. Each *Delta Science Module* emphasizes basic science concepts and science content while developing students' process skills and increasing their appreciation for both the natural world and technology.

Why Hands-On Science? Children are fascinated by the world and enjoy opportunities to explore it. Students can best acquire science concepts and skills by means of an inquiry-based, hands-on approach that focuses on the processes and techniques of discovery. Hands-on science also helps to develop positive attitudes towards science, and enhances mathematical, social, artistic, and language skills. The *Delta Science Modules* promote scientific literacy and provide opportunities for students to satisfy their innate curiosity as they develop effective techniques for observing, questioning, and testing basic scientific concepts.

Problem Solving. At the heart of the *Delta Science Modules* are the types of questions that children ask as they explore the world around them. **What will happen?** Open-ended questions encourage students to explore and begin to gather evidence. **How and why does it happen?** Students develop ideas and make inferences based on their observations while developing effective experimental techniques. **What will happen next?** Students are asked to predict, based on their observations, what will happen as the result of further experimentation. They then are encouraged to compare their results to their predictions. This, in turn, may provide the basis for more questions and additional investigations. Throughout this sequence, related content and terms are introduced.

The goal of the *Delta Science Modules* is to provide the students of today with experiences that will enable them to become scientifically literate contributors to tomorrow's society.

Components

Each *Delta Science Module* enables you to make effective and efficient use of your most valuable resource—time with your students. The components of the program are designed to provide you with the tools to help you in your role as the facilitator of learning.

Teacher's Guide. The Teacher's Guide helps to prepare you for the activities by providing a brief *Overview* of the entire module and a list of the objectives for each activity. A *Schedule of Activities* is included to help you plan ahead for your science sessions. The introduction to each module ends with *Background Information*, *Advance Preparation*, and *Materials Management* strategies to help you prepare for the activities. More detailed information in those three important areas is presented in the activities.

The information included in each activity provides you with a complete lesson plan. The components of each activity are described on the following page.

Objectives describe the focus and goals for the activity.

Schedule lets you know how much time to allow for the activity, and how many Sessions are necessary.

Vocabulary lists new vocabulary words introduced in the activity and defined in the Glossary.

Materials list indicates the items used in the activity, and the quantity required for each student or team.

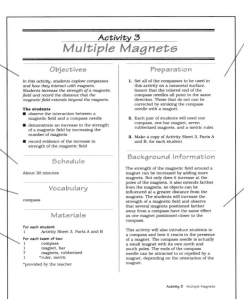

Preparation provides detailed instructions explaining what you will need to prepare prior to beginning the activity.

Background Information explains related science content information.

Teaching Suggestions include all of the directions for you and your students to complete the activity. The numbered steps include highlighted sample questions to assist you in leading classroom discussions.

Science at Home suggests follow-up activities that students can conduct at home.

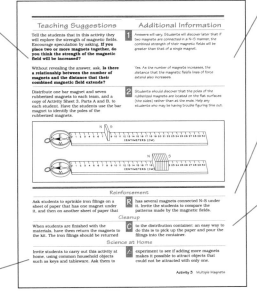

Additional Information includes sample answers for discussion questions, tips to help you facilitate the activity, and safety reminders where appropriate.

Reinforcement provides activity suggestions for students who need more experience with the concepts presented in the activities.

Cleanup provides instructions to facilitate cleanup and the return of materials to the kit.

Connections at the end of each activity provide suggestions for extending and applying the concepts presented in the activity. Activities or discussion topics include *Science Challenges; Science, Technology, and Society; Science and Careers;* and subject integration in the areas of *Language Arts, Mathematics, the Arts, Social Studies,* and *Health.*

Activity Sheets. Photocopy masters for all activity sheets are included at the end of the Teacher's Guide. The activity sheets are used by students to record and interpret results, and in some cases include procedures for students to follow. You may either collect the activity sheets at the end of each activity, or have students maintain a portfolio to which they may add each activity sheet as it is completed. Maintaining the activity sheets in a portfolio will enable you to review the work of each student, and also is an excellent way to provide parents with information about students' accomplishments in science. Completed activity sheets may also be used to assess a student's progress.

Performance Based Assessment. Each *Delta Science Module* Teacher's Guide includes a comprehensive assessment activity so that you may assess each student upon completion of the module. The assessment activity consists of three sections and is designed to assess each student's ability to work with materials, and apply the major concepts and content introduced in the module.

Materials Kit. Each *Delta Science Module* includes almost all the materials necessary to carry out the activities with a class of 32 students. Common items and perishables are not included. Prepaid *Living Material Order Cards* are included for those modules that require live organisms. The order cards must be sent to Delta Education 4 weeks before beginning the activities that include the use of the organisms.

The materials are conveniently packaged, and placed in easily accessible, durable plastic storage drawers housed in a sturdy storage module. The Materials List on page 3 of this guide indicates the quantity of each item included in the kit, and which items you will need to supply. Consumable items are indicated on this list and included in a *Refill Kit* that can be ordered from Delta Education. A convenient *Replacement Parts List* is also available so that individual items can be ordered.

Classroom Management

Materials. You may want to familiarize yourself with the kit materials before beginning the module. The contents of each drawer are listed on the drawer labels. We suggest that you refer to the Materials List on page 3 of this guide as you review the materials in each drawer.

Before beginning each activity, review the Materials list and the Preparation required for the activity. The Materials list indicates which items will be used in the activity, how many of each item will be needed for each individual and each student team, and the size of each team. We recommend that you ask student helpers to assist you in locating materials and preparing for each activity.

Distribution Stations. The most efficient way to distribute materials during an activity is to set up distribution stations from which students can obtain materials as needed. If space in your classroom is limited, you may have room for only one station. If you have more space, we recommend setting up two or three distribution stations, each containing about half or one-third of all the materials listed in the Materials list for each activity. In this way, each distribution station will contain all of the different items used in the activity, and students will not need to visit more than one station to obtain all of their materials.

Cooperative Learning. The *Delta Science Modules* encourage and promote cooperative learning strategies. The quantity of materials included in each kit allows small groups of students to investigate phenomena and each student to make observations and report what they have learned. The interaction between team members is an integral part of each activity and enhances individual outcomes.

Overview

Students begin this Delta Science Module by exploring the components of our Solar System. They become familiar with the names of the planets and then research and share information on each planet.

In Activity 2, students construct and manipulate a model satellite system to help them visualize how gravity holds a satellite in orbit around another object in space. Students relate their observations to Earth's orbit around the Sun and the Moon's orbit around the Earth.

In the next activity, students build a setup that enables them to draw an ellipse. They discover that the shape of a planet's orbit is not a circle, but an ellipse.

In Activity 4, students are introduced to terms that identify the parts of a circle and to a tool for drawing circles—a drawing compass. With the drawing compass, they draw circles of specified sizes. Students will apply this skill in a later activity when they construct models of the planets.

In Activity 5, students develop an understanding of the concepts of scale, ratio, and relative size. They measure scale drawings of familiar objects and calculate, using scale ratios, the actual sizes of the objects represented. They also learn to determine the relative sizes of large-scale objects.

In Activity 6, students apply their experience in making circles and scale drawings to construct a scale model of each of the nine planets of the Solar System. The models help them visualize the enormous differences in size among the actual planets.

Activity 7 helps students apply what they have learned about scale and relative size in order to grasp the concept of relative distance. They measure distances from one object to several others in the classroom,

decide on a scale, and draw their own scale maps. Students use their maps to compare and discuss the relative distances of the objects from one another.

In Activity 8, students construct a 7.5-m (25-ft) classroom model of the Solar System, using their planet models from Activity 6. They place their planet models at scaled distances from an arc representing the Sun.

Students use satellite models and light sources in Activity 9 to demonstrate planetary rotation and revolution. They learn that one rotation of a planet about its axis constitutes a day and that one revolution of a planet around the Sun constitutes a year. Later they role-play planets revolving around the Sun and realize that the farther away a planet is from the Sun, the larger its orbit, and the longer its year.

Activity 10 introduces students to some of the other satellites that exist in our Solar System—asteroids, meteoroids, and comets. Discussions involve descriptions of these minor satellites and how they differ from one another.

Students explore stars beyond our Solar System in Activity 11. They discuss distances of stars from Earth and from one another in terms of light years. They find that stars differ in size, brightness, and temperature.

Students investigate constellations in Activity 12. They discuss myths and how ancient peoples used them to explain in supernatural terms events on Earth. After viewing projected transparencies of the night sky in each of the four seasons, students use tubes and patterns to construct models with which they can view and identify several constellations. Then they use their imaginations to create a myth about the origin of one of the constellations.

Overview Chart

Activity	The students . . .
1 Meet Our Solar System	• discuss the concept of *system* • gather, record, and present data about the Sun and planets • arrange labels of the planets in order of their distance from the Sun
2 Earth Orbits the Sun	• are introduced to the concept of *satellite* • build and manipulate a model satellite system • relate the concept of *gravity* to the orbits of satellites
3 Orbits Are Not Circles	• compare and contrast a circle with an ellipse • construct and use a setup to draw a circle • modify the setup to draw an ellipse
4 Making Circles	• explore the concepts of *radius* and *diameter* • practice making circles with a drawing compass • measure and draw circles of different sizes
5 Scale and Relative Size	• explore the relationships among metric units of measure • calculate actual heights of objects drawn to scale • determine relative size using scale drawings of familiar objects • discover that drawings of objects must be made to the same scale in order to determine their relative sizes
6 Modeling Planet Sizes	• calculate the radii for scale models of the planets • make a scale model of each planet • compare the relative sizes of the planets
7 Scale and Relative Distance	• relate the concept of relative size to relative distance • calculate distances on a map using scaled distance data • create a scale drawing from actual distance measurements
8 Modeling Planet Distances	• discuss which scale would be appropriate for modeling the Solar System in the classroom • make and display a model of the Solar System that shows the relative distances of the planets from the Sun • compare distances of the various planets from the Sun
9 Days and Years	• distinguish between rotation and revolution • construct and operate a model to demonstrate planetary rotation • role-play planets revolving around the Sun
10 Asteroids, Meteoroids, and Comets	• investigate asteroids, meteoroids, and comets • examine a frozen model of a comet head • draw a comet at various points on its elliptical orbit
11 Star Light, Star Bright	• use the term *light-year* in discussing distances from Earth to distant stars • investigate the relative brightness of light sources at various distances • are introduced to the concepts of *galaxy* and *universe*
12 Stories in the Sky	• observe seasonal changes in the position of constellations as viewed from Earth • construct constellation models and identify several constellations • write a fictional story about the origin of a constellation

Materials List

Qty		Description	Qty		Description
18		balls, foam, drilled	1	c	tape, masking
16		batteries, AA-size	1		transparency, Fall Sky
16		batteries, D-size	1		transparency, Spring Sky
2		bulbs, 100-watt	1		transparency, Summer Sky
17		cardboard, square, 34 cm x 34 cm	1		transparency, Winter Sky
16		compasses, drawing	17	c	tubes, cardboard
1		Constellation Patterns	17		tubes, plastic
8	c	cups, paper, soufflé, 2-oz	1		tweezers
8		cups, plastic, 7-oz	17		washers
1	c	fishing line, 100 m			
8		flashlights	1		teacher's guide
2	c	glue, 4 oz			
1		guide, reference, *Solar System*			*Teacher provided items*
10	c	index cards, 20 cm x 20 cm	–		balls, assorted
1		labels, Names of Planets (9)	1		chalk
2		light sources	8		crayons, red
8		†metersticks	1		map, local
9		pans, aluminum	17		markers, black
1	c	paper, butcher	–	c	match, safety
17	c	paper, construction, black	1		overhead projector
15	c	paper, construction, blue	–	c	paper, plain
8		penlights	–		pebbles
1		poster, Goldfish and Whale scale drawing	17		pencils
34		push pins	1		safety goggles
16		rulers, metric	16		scissors
1	c	steel wool pads, p/6	–	c	tape, transparent
1	c	string, 75 m	–	c	water, muddy

† = in separate box
c = consumable item

Schedule of Activities

Activity Number and Title	1	2	3	4	5	6	7	8	9	10	11	12	13	14	15
1 Meet Our Solar System	▨														
2 Earth Orbits the Sun		▨													
3 Orbits Are Not Circles			▨												
4 Making Circles				▨											
5 Scale and Relative Size					▨										
6 Modeling Planet Sizes						▨									
7 Scale and Relative Distance							▨ ●								
8 Modeling Planet Distances								▨ ●							
9 Days and Years										▨ ●					
10 Asteroids, Meteoroids, and Comets												▨			
11 Star Light, Star Bright													▨		
12 Stories in the Sky													●	▨	
Assessment															▨

➤ Continuing observation or wait time required

● Advance preparation required

Preparing for the Activities

Background Information

A solar system comprises a star and all the objects that travel around it. Our Solar System includes our Sun (a star) and all its satellites—planets, moons, asteroids, meteoroids, and comets.

Like other stars, our Sun is a huge ball of burning gases that produces tremendous amounts of heat and light. The Sun's radiation affects surface conditions on all its satellites. Surfaces on planets closest to the sun are hot, while the surface of the outermost planet, Pluto, is extremely cold.

The planets, in order beginning with the one closest to the Sun, are Mercury, Venus, Earth, Mars, Jupiter, Saturn, Uranus, Neptune, and Pluto. Some planets, but not all, have their own satellites, or moons.

The path a satellite travels is called an *orbit*. Satellites are held in their orbits around another object by gravity—an attractive force that exists between objects. Because there is gravitational attraction between all objects in space, a satellite's actual orbit is elliptical, not circular, in shape.

Owing to the elliptical shape of orbits, a point exists along every orbit at which a satellite is closest to the object it is orbiting and another point at which it is farthest away. A planet at its closest point to the Sun is said to be at perihelion; at its farthest point it is at aphelion.

A scale model of the Solar System can help us visualize and better comprehend the relative sizes of, and distances between, objects in the system. To create scale models of objects, their actual dimensions must first be reduced, or scaled down. A numerical ratio is used to represent the scale of reduction. For example, the ratio, or scale, of 1 cm:9,000,000 km means that 1 centimeter in the model represents 9 million kilometers in the actual object.

The same scale must be applied to all objects in a system if their relative sizes and distances are to be accurately represented. However, because of the tremendous distances that separate planets from the Sun and from one another, two different scales must be used to model the Solar System in the classroom. One scale serves to model the planets' relative sizes; the other scale serves to model the relative distances of their orbits from the Sun.

Models can also help to demonstrate time periods, such as planetary days and years. A planet spins on an imaginary axle—its axis—that passes through its center. One complete spin, or rotation, is called a day on any planet, regardless of the Earth-time it takes to complete. All planets rotate at different speeds, so the lengths of their days vary considerably.

One complete orbit, or revolution, of a planet around the Sun constitutes a year on that planet, regardless of the Earth-time it takes to complete. Generally speaking, the farther a planet is from the Sun, the longer its year, although planets do travel at different speeds.

Our Solar System contains other satellites besides planets and their moons. Asteroids are tiny planets that orbit the Sun. Meteoroids are small bits of matter that also orbit the Sun. If a meteoroid's orbit brings it too close to a planet, gravity may pull the meteoroid toward the planet's surface. A meteoroid becomes a meteor when it rushes through the atmosphere of a planet and the friction between it and the molecules of the atmosphere cause it to burn white-hot. Any fragment of the meteor that goes on to impact the surface of the planet is then known as a *meteorite.*

Comets, still another type of satellite, are like huge dirty snowballs, a mile or more in diameter, consisting of ice-covered dust and rock particles. As a comet approaches perihelion in its orbit, the Sun's radiation vaporizes its icy surface, sending gases and dust particles streaming away from the comet's head in a shining "tail." Sunlight reflecting off particles in the comet's tail makes the comet visible to us on Earth.

Our Sun is but one of the estimated 100 billion stars in the Milky Way galaxy, which itself is but one of countless massive star clusters scattered through the universe. From Earth we can see other stars in our galaxy besides our Sun. Distances from Earth to these other stars, as well as their distances from one another, are so great that we measure them in light-years. One light-year is the distance light travels in one Earth-year, or about 9.46 trillion km.

The relative distances of stars from Earth cannot be determined by their apparent relative brightness. Lights farther away appear dimmer than nearby lights of equal intensity. However, stars glow at different intensities, so a bright, distant star appears closer to us than a dimmer, nearby star.

People who lived in ancient times often viewed patterns of stars in the night sky as shapes of actual or fictitious persons, animals, or events. Often the images were derived from myths—stories depicting gods and goddesses, heroes and heroines, or celestial battles. The areas of the sky containing these star-patterns are called constellations.

While the patterns of stars in the constellations do not change, Earth's revolution around the Sun causes our view of the constellations in the night sky to change from season to season. Then, after a full year has passed, we see them in their original positions once again.

Advance Preparation

Activity 5 asks that you obtain a scale model—a toy car, boat, train, or doll, for example—to show the class. If possible, find out (or estimate) the scale to which the model was made.

In Activity 6, you will need to obtain and show students an assortment of spherical objects—a BB, a baseball, a basketball, and a marble.

Obtain a local map for use in Activities 7 and 8.

To prepare for Activity 9, decide on an open area of the school yard where the class can role-play the Sun and planets of the Solar System. You will need to refer to Figure 9-3 to determine the largest scaled "orbit" your school yard can accommodate.

Before the day Activity 10 is taught, models of comet heads must be prepared by placing muddy water and pebbles in cups and then freezing the mixture. You may want to use rubber gloves when handling the steel wool in this activity.

Activity 12 will require an overhead projector for transparencies of the night sky in each of the four seasons.

Materials Management

Students will use drawing compasses in Activity 4. If they find it difficult to rotate the pencil point around the metal point of the compass, suggest they hold the compass still and rotate the paper beneath it. As an alternative method, have them hold the metal point in place with one hand while they rotate the pencil point with the other.

You will burn steel wool in Activity 10 to simulate a meteor. As a safety precaution, have a container of water nearby during the demonstration.

Activity 1

Meet Our Solar System

Objectives

In this activity, students are introduced to the concept of a system and begin the investigation of our Solar System. They research facts about each of the planets and present this information to the class.

The students

■ discuss the concept of *system*

■ gather, record, and present data about the Sun and planets

■ arrange labels of the planets in order of their distance from the Sun

Schedule

About 40 minutes

Vocabulary

Earth	Saturn
Jupiter	solar system
Mars	star
Mercury	Sun
mnemonic device	system
Neptune	Uranus
planet	Venus
Pluto	

Materials

For each student
1   Activity Sheet 1, Parts A and B

For each team of two
1   *marker, black
1   ruler, metric

1 pair   *scissors
1 pc   *scrap paper, for glue (optional)

For the class
2 bottles   glue
1   guide, reference, *Solar System*
10   index cards
1 set   labels, Names of Planets
1   *marker, black
9 sht   paper, construction, blue
1 roll   tape, masking

*provided by the teacher

Preparation

1. Make a copy of Activity Sheet 1, Parts A and B, for each student.

2. In the reference guide provided, locate the information about the individual planets. In addition, you may choose to gather other reference books as well. Student teams representing each planet will need access to information pertinent to their planet.

3. Cut eleven 2 cm x 28 cm (about 0.75 in. x 11 in.) strips from each sheet of blue construction paper. Each student will need three 2 cm x 28 cm strips.

4. Label the top of each of nine index cards with the name of a planet (*Mercury, Venus, Earth, Mars, Jupiter, Saturn, Uranus, Neptune, Pluto*). Label a tenth card *Sun*. Leave space under the labels for students to record data.

5. Each team of two will need a pair of scissors, a metric ruler, a black marker, and access to the glue. You may wish to let teams put puddles of glue on pieces of scrap paper for use at their

workstations. The class will need the 10 labeled index cards and the reference information on the Solar System.

Background Information

A system is an interdependent group of items that form a unified whole. In the human body, for example, organs are grouped into different systems—the digestive system, the respiratory system, and so on. Roads, bridges, and vehicles make up a transportation system.

A solar system consists of a star and all the objects that travel around it. A star is a luminous ball of burning gas that produces tremendous amounts of light and heat.

Our Solar System consists of a central star (the Sun) and the planets, moons, asteroids, meteoroids, and comets that travel around it. The planets, in order beginning with the planet closest to the Sun, are Mercury, Venus, Earth, Mars, Jupiter, Saturn, Uranus, Neptune, and Pluto. Refer to Figure 1-1 for statistics on the Sun and the planets.

The Sun radiates tremendous amounts of light and heat through space. The effects of this radiation are felt millions of miles away. Solar light and heat influence the conditions on and near the surfaces of the planets.

The four inner planets—those closest to the Sun—are primarily rocky and metallic in composition, while the four major outer planets—Jupiter to Neptune—are huge, not very dense, and have deep gaseous atmospheres. The outermost planet, Pluto, is much smaller than the other planets and is composed of ice and rock.

Name	Diameter (km)	Atmosphere	Average Distance from Sun (km)	Moons and Rings
Sun	1,392,000	hydrogen	—	—
Mercury	4,878	helium/ sodium	57.8 million	none
Venus	12,100	carbon dioxide/ sulfuric acid	108.2 million	none
Earth	12,756	nitrogen/ oxygen	149.6 million	1 moon
Mars	6,786	carbon dioxide	227.9 million	2 moons
Jupiter	143,200	hydrogen/ helium	778.3 million	16 moons, 1 ring
Saturn	120,536	hydrogen/ helium	1.429 billion	22 moons, 8 rings
Uranus	51,118	hydrogen/ helium	2.871 billion	15 moons, 11 rings
Neptune	49,528	hydrogen/ helium	4.501 billion	8 moons, 4 rings
Pluto	2,400	nitrogen, methane, and carbon monoxide	6 billion	1 moon

Figure 1-1. Solar System data.

Meet Our Solar System

What is a solar system? _____
a star and all the objects that travel around it
_____
_____

What is the name of the star in our Solar System? the Sun

What are the parts of our Solar System?
the Sun and all the planets

How many planets are there in our Solar System? nine

What are the names of the planets in our Solar System, in order beginning with the planet closest to the Sun?
Mercury,
Venus,
Earth,
Mars,
Jupiter,
Saturn,
Uranus,
Neptune,
and Pluto

1. Cut each strip of blue construction paper into three pieces, two 9-cm pieces and one 10-cm piece. With a black marker, write the name of one planet lengthwise on each strip of paper. Use the longest pieces for the longest names.

2. On Part B of the activity sheet, beginning next to the curve that represents the edge of the Sun, arrange your nine labels in the order of each planet's distance from the Sun, just as your teacher did on the board. Glue your labels to the page under the numbers 1 to 9.

Meet Our Solar System

9. Pluto
8. Neptune
7. Uranus
6. Saturn
5. Jupiter
4. Mars
3. Earth
2. Venus
1. Mercury

Sun

Teaching Suggestions

Write *system* on the board and ask, **What do you think a system is?**

Begin a discussion of systems with which students may be familiar, such as a transportation system. Tell them that roads, bridges, and vehicles make up a transportation system.

Discuss the digestive system next. Explain that the human digestive system is made of many body parts and that all these parts must work together in order to accomplish a single task—that of nourishing the body.

Ask, **Can you think of another system? How would it change if one of its parts were missing?**

Write their responses on the board and discuss whether they are systems and, if they are, how such changes would affect them.

Additional Information

1 Accept all responses. A system is a group of items that form a unified whole.

Write the terms *solar system* and *star* near the top of the board, as shown in Figure 1-2. Ask, **What do you think a solar system is?**

2

Accept all answers and speculations.

Explain that *solar* means "relating to the Sun." Tell them a solar system is made up of a star and all the objects that travel around it.

Tell students that a star is a ball of burning gases and that our Sun is a star. Stars give off tremendous amounts of light and heat.

Draw a large circle on the board under the word *Star*, as shown in Figure 1-2. (The labels shown in the figure will be added later.)

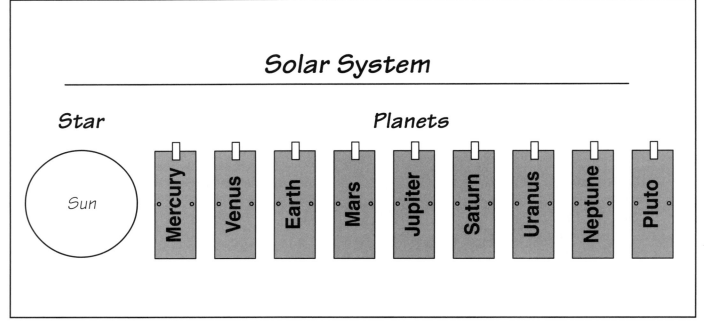

Solar System

Star　　　　　　　　　　　**Planets**

Sun　　Mercury　Venus　Earth　Mars　Jupiter　Saturn　Uranus　Neptune　Pluto

Figure 1-2. Our Solar System.

Ask, **What are the names of some of the objects that travel around the Sun?**

3

Students will probably know the names of many of the planets.

Write *Planets* on the board, as shown in Figure 1-2. Tell students that Earth is one of nine planets that travel around our Sun.

Moons, comets, meteors, and asteroids also travel around the Sun. These types of satellites will be explored in a subsequent activity.

Explain that teams will gather data about the Sun and the planets and then share the information with the rest of the class.

Divide the class into 10 teams.

Tell students that each team will be given an index card labeled with the name of one of the planets or with *Sun*. Each team is to gather data from the reference books about their planet (or the Sun) and record that data on their card.

Ask, **What are some of the facts about the Sun and planets you would like to find out?**

Many students will be interested in information about size, temperature, surface features, and color.

List at least four categories on the board to guide the students' research. Suggest that teams find information regarding size (diameter), composition of atmosphere (if one is present), distance from Sun, presence and number of moons, presence and number of rings, and so on.

Distribute an index card and the reference materials to each team.

Depending on the number of reference books you collected, students will need to share resources.

Allow sufficient time for students to read the material, find the information, and record it on their index cards.

After teams have finished gathering data on the Sun and planets, write the word *Sun* inside the large circle you drew on the board, as shown in Figure 1-2.

Have the team that researched the Sun share the information they found with the rest of the class.

After students have finished presenting the data they found for the Sun, tape the label for Mercury on the board just to the right of the Sun circle.

Invite the team that investigated Mercury to present the facts they discovered about that planet.

After students have finished presenting the data they found for Mercury, tape the label for Venus to the right of that for Mercury.

Invite the team that investigated Venus to present the information they recorded on their card.

Continue calling on the remaining teams until you have taped all the labels to the board and students have all shared their findings with the rest of the class.

Planet labels must be taped to the board in the order shown in Figure 1-2. Call on student teams accordingly.

Tell students they will arrange planet labels on their activity sheets similar to the model on the board.

Divide the class again, this time into teams of two. Give a copy of Activity Sheet 1, Parts A and B, and three strips of blue construction paper to each student. Distribute scissors, a ruler, and a marker to each team. Indicate the location of the glue.

Have students cut each 2 cm x 28 cm strip of paper into three pieces, two pieces 9 cm long and one piece 10 cm long. Tell them to use the marker to write the name of a planet on each paper strip. Suggest they use the longer strips for the longer names. Then have them arrange the labels in the order of their distance from the Sun, following the model on the board. Tell students to glue the labels to their activity sheets.

After students have finished putting the labels of the planets in the proper order on their activity sheets, begin a review of the concepts they have learned. Remind them that a solar system consists of a star and all the objects that travel around it.

Ask, **What is the name of the star in our Solar System?**

the Sun

Ask, **Which two planets are closest to the Sun? Which one is the farthest away?**

Mercury and Venus are closest; Pluto is the farthest planet from the Sun.

Ask, **Which is the largest planet? The smallest?**

Some students will recall information presented by the teams and be able to answer correctly: Jupiter is the largest; Pluto is the smallest.

Ask, **Which one of the planets has no atmosphere at all? Which planet is the only one with an atmosphere that we can breathe?**

Mercury has no atmosphere. The planet Earth is the only one whose atmosphere we can breathe.

Ask, **Do you think if you closed your eyes right now you could name all the planets in order of their distance from the Sun?** Most students will say they would not be able to remember them all.

Tell students there is a trick to help them remember the names of the planets in order. They can make up a sentence with words that begin with the first letter of the name of each planet. Tell them you will give them a couple of examples, and then, if they wish, they can make up their own sentences.

Write the following three sentences on the board:

Many Very Energetic Moms Join Some Unique New Programs.

Many Veggies Eaten Make Jumping Sit-Ups No Problem.

My Very Educated Mother Just Served Us Nine Pickles.

Tell students that memory aids, such as those sentences, are called *mnemonic devices.* Write the term on the board.

Reinforcement

Divide the class into groups of 10 and assign each student a planet name or the role of the Sun. Have groups line themselves up so that their order represents the correct positions of the planets relative to the Sun in our Solar System.

Cleanup

Tell students to return the rulers, glue, and index cards containing data to the kit. Have them discard pieces of scrap paper used for glue. Remove the planet labels from the board, discard the pieces of masking tape, and return the labels and the roll of tape to the kit.

Science at Home

Have students discuss the systems they have in their homes, such as electrical, plumbing, cable television, security alarm, and so on.

Connections

Science Extension

As a long-term project throughout most of this module, have the 10 student teams continue to gather information about the Sun and planets. Give each team an opportunity to present its information to the rest of the class, beginning with the Sun in this activity and proceeding through the nine planets in order in Activities 2–10. Also have each team record its information on a class master chart of the Solar System. In addition to the data given in Figure 1-1, teams could record the planets' day lengths and year lengths (from Activity 9), each body's diameter and gravity relative to Earth's (Science and Math, Activity 5), and its distance from Earth (Science and Math, Activity 7). Additional information about each planet is given in the first Science Extension for Activities 2–10, as it is for the Sun below.

Additional Facts About the Sun
Volume (Earth = 1): 1,306,000
Mass (Earth = 1): 333,000
Density (water = 1): 1.41
Surface temperature: 10,000°F (5,540°C)
Composition: radioactive core, photosphere, chromosphere, corona
Distinctive features: sunspots, solar flares

Science and the Arts

Suggest that students make colorful pictures or three-dimensional models of the Sun based on photographs and illustrations they have found in library books and science textbooks. Some students may want to make cross-sectional diagrams or models that show the Sun's layers: the inner core, the thicker photosphere, the thinner chromosphere, and the outer corona that extends for millions of miles into space.

Science and Health

Tell students that our bodies make vitamin D when our skin is exposed to sunlight. Encourage students to find out about the functions of vitamin D in the human body and the diseases caused by a vitamin D deficiency. Also ask students to find out what foods are good sources of dietary vitamin D.

Science and Language Arts

Perhaps the most commonly used mnemonic device for recalling the names and order of the planets is *My Very Easy Method: Just Stand Under North Pole.* You may want to teach this device to students. (Caution them not to add "the" before "North Pole.") Explain that the *y* in "My" and in "Mercury" will help them remember that Mercury, not Mars, is first. Also ask them to suggest mnemonic devices they use to help them recall other types of information—for example, the simple rhyme *i before e except after c* in spelling.

Science, Technology, and Society

Tell students that in June 1990, NASA released six extraordinary photographs taken by the space probe *Voyager 1.* These photographs were extraordinary because they were the first ever taken from outside the Solar System. The pictures showed six planets—Venus, Earth, Jupiter, Saturn, Uranus, and Neptune—as a space traveler approaching the Sun would see them. Mercury was too close to the Sun to be seen in the pictures, Pluto was too far away, and Mars was obscured by bright sunlight. Find (or ask students to find) examples of these photographs in books. One good source is *Voyager: Exploring the Outer Planets* by Joan Marie Verba (Lerner Publications, 1991).

Activity 2
Earth Orbits the Sun

Objectives

Students model and demonstrate an orbiting satellite. They learn that the gravitational force between the Sun and its satellites creates the planetary orbits.

The students
- are introduced to the concept of *satellite*
- build and manipulate a model satellite system
- relate the concept of *gravity* to the orbits of satellites

Schedule

About 40 minutes

Vocabulary

force	moon
gravitational attraction	orbit
gravity	satellite

Materials

For each student
1   Activity Sheet 2

For each team of two
1   ball, foam, drilled
1   tube, plastic
1   washer

For the class
2   balls, foam, drilled
1 spool   fishing line
1 pair   *scissors
1   tube, plastic

1   washer
*provided by the teacher

Preparation

1. Make a copy of Activity Sheet 2 for each student.

2. Cut a 1-m (about 3-ft) length of fishing line for each team of two and another for your demonstration model.

3. Make a satellite system model. To construct one, tie one end of a 1-m length of fishing line to the washer. Thread the other end of the line through the plastic tube and then through the hole in the ball. Tie this end around the ball as shown in Figure 2-1. Grasping the plastic tube as shown in the figure, raise your fist above your head and move it in small circles so that the ball swings around your fist. The ball represents a satellite in orbit.

4. Each team of two will need a foam ball, a washer, a plastic tube, and a 1-m length of fishing line.

Background Information

An object that travels around a larger object in space is called a *satellite*. All the planets in our Solar System are satellites of our Sun. A moon is a satellite of a planet. Earth's Moon is one of many satellite moons in the Solar System.

A *force* is a push or a pull on an object. *Gravity* is an attractive force that exists between objects.

The *mass* of an object is a measure of how much material it contains. All objects have mass. The magnitude of the force of attraction between two objects depends on the mass of both objects and the distance between them. The greater the combined mass of the two objects, the greater the force of attraction between them. The greater the distance between the two objects, the lesser the force of attraction between them.

This force of attraction is what keeps the planets in *orbit* around the Sun. It is also what keeps moons and all smaller satellites in orbit around the planets.

The shape of a satellite's orbit is determined by the *gravitational attraction* between it and the object it is orbiting and, to a lesser degree, by the gravitational attraction between it and other nearby objects.

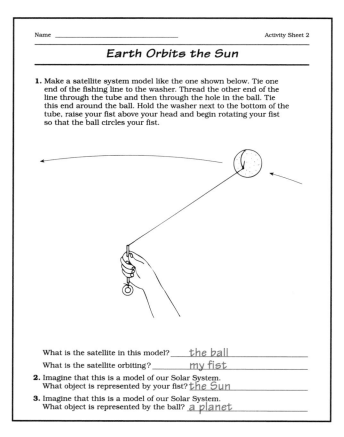

Earth Orbits the Sun

1. Make a satellite system model like the one shown below. Tie one end of the fishing line to the washer. Thread the other end of the line through the tube and then through the hole in the ball. Tie this end around the ball. Hold the washer next to the bottom of the tube, raise your fist above your head and begin rotating your fist so that the ball circles your fist.

What is the satellite in this model? ___the ball___
What is the satellite orbiting? ___my fist___

2. Imagine that this is a model of our Solar System. What object is represented by your fist? the Sun

3. Imagine that this is a model of our Solar System. What object is represented by the ball? a planet

Teaching Suggestions

Demonstrate the satellite system model to the class. Hold the tube above your head and move your fist so that the ball swings in a circle.

1

Additional Information

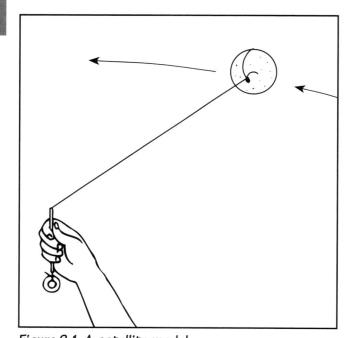

Figure 2-1. A satellite model.

Ask, **What is the ball doing? What is the ball traveling around?**

Responses will vary, but encourage those that mention that the ball is moving in a circle and that it is traveling around your fist.

Write the words *satellite* and *orbit* on the board. Tell students that a satellite is an object that travels around a larger object and that an orbit is the path the satellite takes as it moves around that object.

Explain that the term *orbit* is also used as a verb meaning "to travel the path of the orbit."

Ask, **In this model, what is the satellite?**

the ball

Ask, **What is the ball orbiting? What is the shape of the orbit?**

The ball is traveling around your fist in a circular orbit.

2

Remind students that a solar system is made up of a star and the objects that travel around it. Ask, **Knowing what you know about our Solar System, what does my fist represent?**

the Sun

Ask, **If my fist is the Sun, what is the name of one object that the ball could represent?**

The name of any planet would be a correct response.

Explain that all the planets are satellites because they all travel around, or orbit, the Sun.

Asteroids, meteoroids, and comets are other types of satellites and will be discussed in a later activity.

Ask, **Can you think of another type of satellite—one that orbits Earth?**

Most students will name the Moon, though many will know that artificial satellites also orbit Earth.

Write *moon* on the board and explain that a moon is a satellite that orbits a planet. Our Moon is a satellite of Earth. Also in orbit around Earth are a number of artificial satellites used for communication, weather reporting, and space observation.

3

Give a copy of Activity Sheet 2 to each student. Distribute a pencil, a foam ball, a washer, a plastic tube, and a 1-m length of fishing line to each team.

Tell students to build and operate the satellite model system and then complete Activity Sheet 2.

Offer help as needed in building the models.

When all students have completed the activity sheet, ask, **What keeps the ball from flying off across the room when you spin it around?**

4 the string

What do you think keeps Earth and the other planets from flying off into space away from the Sun?

Accept all speculations.

Write the terms *force, gravity,* and *gravitational attraction* on the board. Introduce the terms by explaining that force is a push or a pull on an object. Gravity is a force that exists between objects.

The force of gravity causes objects to be attracted to one another. This is called *gravitational attraction.*

The gravitational attraction between the Sun and the planets keeps them from flying off into space.

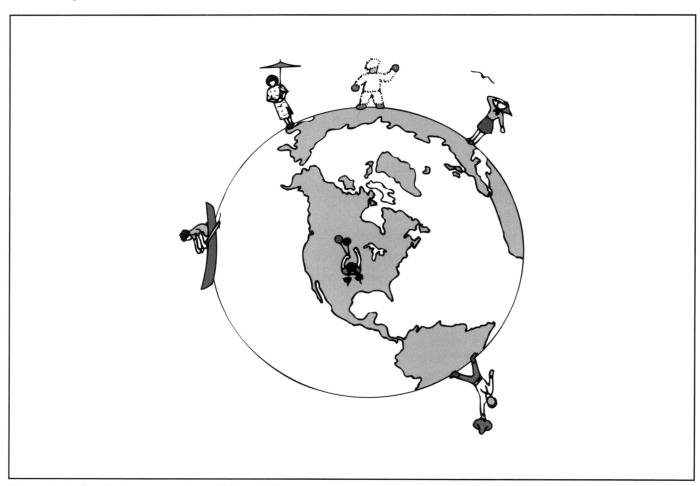

Figure 2-2. Gravity keeps us from flying off into space.

Hold a foam ball at shoulder level and let it fall to the floor. Ask, **What happened to the ball? Why?**

Explain to students that gravity acts between these two objects—the ball and the Earth—just as it acts between the Sun and the Earth. There is a gravitational attraction between them.

Ask, **What effect does Earth's gravity have on your body?**

Students may suggest that gravity caused the ball to fall straight down to the floor.

Students may say that gravity keeps them on the ground or that it keeps them from flying off into space.

Reinforcement

Encourage students to create other satellite models using different materials. Have them identify the objects in their model and verify that one is in fact a satellite of the other.

Cleanup

Have students return the intact satellite system models to the kit. Return the demonstration model you made as well. Unused fishing line should be replaced in the kit.

Connections

Science Extension

Ask the "Mercury" team to report additional information they have found and to record Mercury's data on the class master chart.

Additional Facts About Mercury
Volume (Earth = 1): 0.056
Mass (Earth = 1): 0.055
Density (water = 1): 5.43
Surface temperature: –292°F to +800°F
    (–180°C to +425°C)
Composition: iron and nickel core, rocky
    mantle
Distinctive features: surface is pitted with
    impact craters, like surface of Earth's
    moon

Find a large drawing or photograph of the moon with its features labeled, and make a photocopy for each student. Ask students to look at the moon when it is full or close to full and find as many of the features as they can. Encourage them to use binoculars or telescopes if they have access to them. (Note: You may want to include this activity when the class observes the night sky as suggested in the Science Extension for Activity 12.)

Science and Language Arts

Challenge students to list as many song titles and lyrics as they can that refer to the Sun, the Moon, or a planet. Encourage them to ask older family members and friends to suggest additional titles and lyrics that they may not be familiar with themselves.

Science and Social Studies

Suggest that students find out who Galileo was and what he did that was so important for our understanding of the Solar System. (Galileo was the first person, in the early 1600s, to use the newly invented telescope to study the planets. He proved that the Sun does not orbit Earth, as commonly believed at that time, but that Earth orbits the Sun. Galileo also discovered Jupiter's largest moons.)

Science, Technology, and Society

Encourage interested students to find out about various types of artificial satellites that orbit Earth. For example, *Landsat* takes pictures of Earth that are used in making maps, studying ecological conditions, and looking for oil and mineral supplies. Ships and aircraft use signals from *Navstar* to plot journeys and identify their location. Weather satellites relay photographs of Earth to weather stations on Earth's surface, where computers interpret the information to help predict weather conditions. Communications satellites relay television, radio, and telephone signals around the world.

Students might enjoy doing the following activity to see how communication satellites work. Use lumps of clay to stand a mirror on a table near the open classroom door. Ask one student to stand somewhere in the hallway where he or she can see the mirror, and ask a second student to stand somewhere in the classroom and shine a flashlight at the mirror. Let the two students adjust their positions until the student in the hallway can see the light beam without seeing the student holding the flashlight. Let other pairs of students also try the activity. Explain that in this same way, a signal sent to an orbiting satellite is bounced back to a receiver on Earth thousands of miles from the sender. Also point out that the mirror-and-flashlight setup is a model of the way a communications satellite works.

Activity 3
Orbits Are Not Circles

Objectives

In this activity, students discover that planetary orbits are not circles. They construct a device that enables them to draw ellipses, shapes that more closely resemble the actual paths of planets around the Sun.

The students

■ compare and contrast a circle with an ellipse

■ construct and use a setup to draw a circle

■ modify the setup to draw an ellipse

Schedule

About 40 minutes

Vocabulary

aphelion	foci (fō•sī or fō•kī)
circle	focus (plural: foci)
ellipse	perihelion

Materials

For each student
1	Activity Sheet 3
1 sht	*paper, plain

For each team of two
1	cardboard, square
1	*pencil
2	push pins
1	ruler, metric

For the class
1	cardboard, square
1	*model, satellite (from Activity 2)
1 sht	*paper, plain
1	*pencil
2	push pins
1 pair	*scissors
1 ball	string
1 roll	tape, masking

*provided by the teacher

Preparation

1. Make a copy of Activity Sheet 3 for each student.

2. Cut a 25-cm (about 10-in.) length of string for each team of two. Tie the ends of the string in a secure knot to form a loop. Stretched out, the loop should measure no more than 10 cm (about 4 in.). Trim off the ends of the string above the knot.

3. Construct a demonstration circle- and ellipse-making setup (refer to Figure 3-1). Tape a piece of plain white paper to one of the corrugated cardboard squares from the kit. Use a metric ruler to measure and draw a line lengthwise down the center of the paper. Put a dot at the midpoint of the line and label it *C*. Measure 4 cm (about 1.6 in.) from *C* along the line and make another dot. Label this dot *X*. Measure 4 cm from *C* along the line in the other direction and make a third dot. Label this dot *S*.

   To draw a circle, press a push pin into the dot labeled *C*. Leave just enough space under the head of the push pin for the string loop. Place the string loop under the head of the push pin. Place the tip of the pencil in the loop and pull gently to take up the slack. Keeping gentle tension on the string, draw a circle as you move the pencil around the push pin.

To draw an ellipse, stick push pins into dots S and X and place the same string loop around them both (refer to Figure 3-2). Insert the tip of the pencil into the loop and pull gently to take up the slack. Maintaining gentle tension on the loop of string, draw a line as you move the pencil around the two push pins. Practice using the setup to make circles and ellipses so that you can assist students later.

4. Each team of two will need a piece of cardboard, two push pins, two pieces of plain paper, a metric ruler, a string loop, and access to the roll of masking tape.

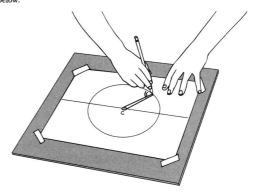
Background Information

A *circle* is a closed curve with all points along the curve the same distance from the center. The center point of a circle is known as the *focus*.

Although the shape of the orbit made by the satellite system model in Activity 2 was a circle, the actual orbit of a satellite in space is an *ellipse*—a shape like a flattened circle.

The points along an elliptical orbit are not all the same distance from a common center. Ellipses have two centers, or *foci*. Elliptical orbits are caused by the gravitational pull of all the objects in a system on one another.

At one point in its elliptical orbit, a planet is closer to the Sun than at any other point. At this point, the planet is said to be at *perihelion*. At the point at which a planet is farthest from the Sun, it is at *aphelion*.

Teaching Suggestions

		Additional Information

Demonstrate again the satellite system model constructed in Activity 2. Review with the class the concepts of *orbit* and *satellite*. **1**

While spinning the model, ask, **What shape would you draw if you were to draw the orbit of the satellite in this model?**

Most students will say they would draw a circle.

Tell students they will construct a setup with which they can draw a circle.

Demonstrate for students how to use the setup to draw a circle. Label the shape you have drawn *Circle.* Tell students that both members of a team will share a setup but that each student will draw on his or her own piece of paper. **2**

Give each student a copy of Activity Sheet 3. Divide the class into teams of two and distribute a cardboard square, a string loop, a metric ruler, a push pin, two sheets of plain paper, and a pencil to each team. Have the roll of masking tape available. **3**

Go over the directions with the teams for Step 1 on the activity sheet, as follows: Tell teams to place the sheet of paper in the center of the cardboard square and tape down the corners. Tell them to use their ruler and pencil to measure and draw a line lengthwise down the center of the paper. Have them measure and make a dot at the midpoint of the line. Tell them to label the dot *C*.

The line need not be down the exact center of the paper.

Tell teams to measure 4 cm (about 1.6 in.) from the *C* along the line, make another dot, and label this dot *X*. Then have them measure 4 cm from *C* along the line in the other direction, make another dot, and label it *S*.

Have the teams press the push pin into the dot labeled *C*. Tell them to place the string loop around the push pin. Have them place the tip of the pencil in the loop and pull outward gently to take up the slack. Have

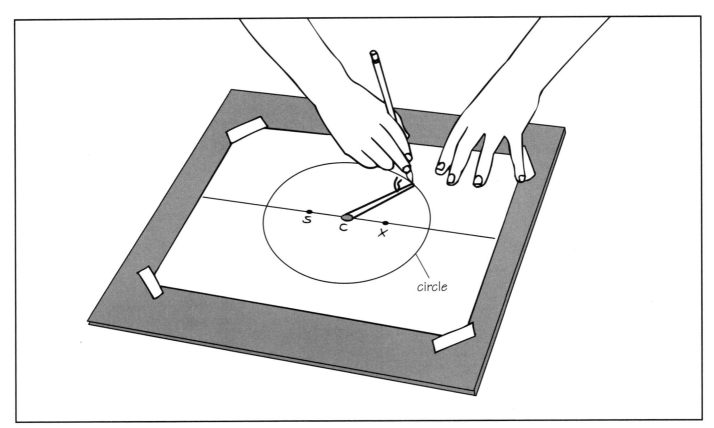

Figure 3-1. Drawing a circle.

them maintain tension on the string as they move the pencil around the push pin to draw a circle.

Have teams use the setups to make circles. Remind them that they should draw circles on their own pieces of paper. Suggest that each student tape a piece of paper to one side of the cardboard. Pairs of students can then alternate use of the cardboard by flipping it over.

Have the students label the shape they have drawn by writing the word *Circle* next to the closed curve.

After teams have finished drawing circles, write the word *focus* on the board. Tell students that the center point of a circle is called the focus. Ask, **What letter labels the focus of your circle?**

Hold up one of the teams' setups and point to several places along the circle. Explain that all the points along the curved line of a circle are the same distance from the focus.

Tell students that they must leave just enough space under the head of the push pin so the loop can move freely around underneath it.

4 Some students may need assistance, but most will be able to draw circles. Tell students if they pull the loop too hard with the pencil, they may pull the push pin out of the cardboard. If that should happen, have them reinsert the push pin and try again without pulling quite so hard. Have them raise the push pin slightly if the string loop does not rotate freely.

Each student will draw another shape on the same piece of paper, so labeling both shapes as they draw them will enable students to identify them later.

5

the letter C

Ask, **Does this shape look like the shape of the path of the foam ball in the satellite system model?**   Yes.

Write the word *ellipse* on the board. Explain that an ellipse is like a flattened circle. Tell students that the actual shape of a satellite's orbit resembles an ellipse, not a circle. As a satellite moves through space, it interacts with the gravitational forces of other objects, besides the Sun, which influence the shape of its path.

Tell students they will modify their setups to draw a shape that very closely resembles the shape of a planetary orbit.

Show students how to modify their setups. Move the push pin from *C* to the dot labeled *S*. Then add a second push pin at dot *X*. Tell students to use the string loop and pencil in the same way as they did when they drew circles except that now the string will be around two push pins.

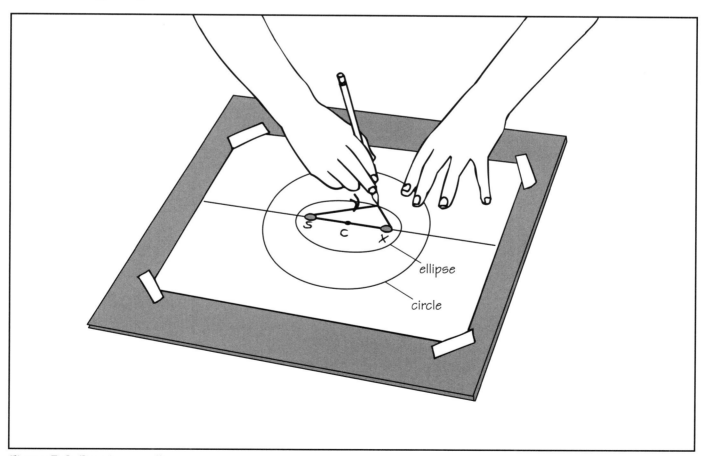

Figure 3-2. Drawing an ellipse.

Demonstrate how to use the setup to make this new shape, and then show the students the new shape that you have drawn.

Remind students not to pull too hard on the string loop with the pencil or the push pins may be dislodged.

8

Give a second push pin to each team. Go over the directions with the teams for Step 2 on the activity sheet. Tell them to modify their setups as you did in the demonstration and to draw their ellipses on the same sheet of paper with the circle. Remind them to label the new shape *Ellipse*.

After teams have finished drawing ellipses, ask, **How would you describe this shape?**

Most students will say that it looks like a flattened circle. Accept all descriptions.

Remind students that a circle has one focus. Tell students that the plural of the word *focus* is *foci*.

Choose either of two acceptable pronunciations— fō•sī or fō•kī—and use it consistently throughout the activities. Have students pronounce the word aloud.

Ask, **How many foci does an ellipse have?**

two

What are the foci labeled on your setup?

S and X

Explain that the distance between the foci on their setup determines the flatness of the ellipse. The farther apart the foci, the flatter the ellipse.

Remind students that all the planets orbit one object, the Sun, but that the shape of planetary orbits is elliptical. Orbits are ellipses rather than circles because they are shaped by the interactions of gravitational pull among the many objects in the Solar System.

9

Have students label dot *C* with the word *Sun*. Tell students that the Sun could be depicted almost anywhere along the center line within the ellipse but that at position *C* the ellipse most resembles the shape of a planetary orbit.

Tell them to imagine that the ellipse they have drawn is Earth's orbit. Ask, **Is Earth the same distance from the Sun at all times during its orbit?**

No.

Where is it closest to the Sun? Farthest from the Sun?

Write the terms *perihelion* and *aphelion* on the board. Tell students that the point in the orbit where Earth is closest to the Sun is called *perihelion* and the point at which it is farthest is called *aphelion*.

Have students complete Activity Sheet 3.

Students can point on their models to the respective areas on the ellipse where the arc is closest to and farthest from focus C.

Reinforcement

Draw a picture of a bicycle on the board (or display an enlarged photo or drawing of a bicycle without a chain guard) and ask students to identify the two foci of the

 ellipse made by the bicycle chain. (the center of the rear wheel and the center of the sprocket)

Cleanup

Have students entitle their papers *Circle and Ellipse*, write their names on them, and then remove the sheets from the cardboard and save them for use in later activities. Have students return the squares of cardboard,

 metric rulers, push pins, and string loops to the kit. The ball of string and roll of masking tape should also be replaced in the kit.

Science at Home

Have students identify and make a list of elliptical objects and near-elliptical shapes they can find around their homes.

 Possibilities include eggs, handles of scissors or coffee cups, bathroom sink tops, and so on.

Connections

Science Extension

Ask the "Venus" team to report additional information they have found and to record Venus's data on the class master chart.

Additional Facts About Venus
Volume (Earth = 1): 0.86
Mass (Earth = 1): 0.815
Density (water = 1): 5.25
Surface temperature: 870°F (465°C)
Composition: iron core, rocky mantle
Distinctive features: brightest "star" in the sky, known as the Morning Star or Evening Star; carbon dioxide atmosphere produces extreme greenhouse effect, making Venus the hottest planet in the Solar System; surface temperature is hot enough to melt lead; volcanic lava flows cover surface; constant lightning in atmosphere

Science and the Arts

Obtain a copy of the children's book *To Space & Back*, astronaut Sally Ride's first-person account of her space-shuttle trips in orbit around Earth (Sally Ride with Susan Okie; Lothrup, Lee, & Shepard; 1986). Give students time to read the book, then ask them to work in teams to write and perform short skits dramatizing various scenes described in the book.

Science and Careers

Invite a professional astronomer or an experienced hobbyist to visit the class and describe his or her work or hobby. Ask the visitor to bring a telescope, demonstrate how it is used, and let students use it to observe distant objects, including the moon if it is visible in the daytime sky. Encourage students to ask the visitor questions about how he or she first became interested in astronomy, the education or training needed, and any other issues that interest them.

Science and Language Arts

Ask students to use a dictionary to find out where the terms *perihelion* and *aphelion* come from. (from the Greek *peri*, meaning "near, around"; *ap-*, "away from"; and *helios*, "sun") Also ask them to explain the meanings of two other words they may be familiar with that contain the prefix *peri-*: *periscope* and *perimeter.*

Science and Social Studies

Write the words *astronomy* and *astrology* on the board. Explain that astronomy is the scientific study of the objects in the universe, whereas astrology is the nonscientific study of the planets based on the belief that their positions in the sky control or influence people's lives and events on Earth. Encourage students to read about the work and beliefs of ancient astrologers in different cultures. Point out that although astrology has no basis in scientific fact, early astrologers did make discoveries that contributed to the development of scientific knowledge about objects in the sky.

Science, Technology, and Society

Many children's library books about the Solar System contain dramatic close-up photographs—taken by space probes such as *Mariner*, *Viking*, and *Magellan*—that show the planets' surface features. Let students examine such photographs and compare the different appearances of the planets. If possible, obtain and display a set of planet posters that include surface photographs as well as photographs of each entire planet.

Activity 4
Making Circles

Objectives

Students become familiar with the parts of a circle and a tool with which they can draw circles. They will apply this knowledge in a later activity when they measure and draw circles of various diameters to model the planets.

The students

■ explore the concepts of *radius* and *diameter*

■ practice making circles with a drawing compass

■ measure and draw circles of different sizes

Schedule

About 50 minutes

Vocabulary

circumference
diameter
drawing compass
radius (plural: radii)

Materials

For each student
1	Activity Sheet 4
1 sht	*paper, entitled *Circle and Ellipse* (from Activity 3)

For each team of two
1	cardboard, square
1	compass, drawing
2 sht	*paper, plain

1	ruler, metric

For the class
1 pc	*chalk
1	meterstick
1 sht	*paper, plain
1 pair	*scissors
1 ball	string
1 roll	tape, masking

*provided by the teacher

Preparation

1. Make a copy of Activity Sheet 4 for each student.

2. Cut a 30-cm (about 12-in.) length of string and tie a loop in one end large enough to accommodate a piece of chalk. During the activity, you will use chalk and this piece of string to draw circles on the board.

3. Each team of two will need their papers entitled *Circle and Ellipse* from Activity 3, a piece of cardboard, two clean sheets of plain paper, a drawing compass, a metric ruler, and access to the roll of masking tape.

Background Information

Celestial objects—stars, planets, moons, asteroids, and so on—are, of course, three-dimensional and generally spherical in shape. Modeling them for teaching purposes in two dimensions on a flat sheet of paper requires constructing circles of specific sizes. For this purpose, it is necessary to know the several components of a circle and how they relate to one another.

A straight line drawn from the focus (center) to any point on the *circumference* (outside curve) of a circle is called the *radius.* The plural of *radius* is *radii* (pronounced (rā•dē•ī). All the radii in any one circle are the same length.

A straight line drawn from any point on the circumference of a circle through its focus to the circumference on the other side of the circle is called the *diameter* of the circle. All the diameters in any one circle are the same length.

A diameter can be thought of as two radii drawn in opposite directions from the focus. The diameter of a circle is equal to twice the length of the radius of that circle.

A *drawing compass* is a mechanical device used to draw circles. To draw a circle, spread the arms of the drawing compass so that the distance between the pencil point and the metal point equals the radius of the circle you want to draw. Grasping the handle at the top, press the metal point of the drawing compass, which will be the focus of the circle, into the paper. Rotate the pencil to draw a circle while keeping the metal point pressed into the paper.

Name _____ Activity Sheet 4

Making Circles

What is the radius of the circle drawn in Activity 3? _about 10 cm_
What is the diameter of that same circle? _____ about 20 cm

1. Tape a sheet of paper to the cardboard. Draw a dot near the center of the paper. Label the dot *C*. Put the point of the compass into the dot labeled *C*, as shown in the illustration below.

2. Use the compass to draw a circle that has a radius of 5 cm. Use your ruler to measure. What is the diameter of this circle? _10 cm_

3. Make two circles—one with a radius of 3 cm and the other with a radius of 10 cm.
   What is the diameter of the circle with a 3-cm radius? _6 cm_
   What is the diameter of the circle with a 10-cm radius? _20 cm_

4. Label the radius of each circle with the word *radius*.
   Do you see a relationship between the lengths of a radius and a diameter in each circle? Explain.
   _____A radius is half the length of a diameter._
   _or_ _____A diameter is twice the length of a radius._

Teaching Suggestions

1

Remind students of the way they drew a circle in Activity 3 using a push pin, a string loop, and a pencil.

Draw a circle on the board, as follows: Place a piece of chalk through the loop at one end of the 30-cm string. Hold the other end of the string against the board with the finger of one hand. With your other hand, stretch the string taut and draw a circle with the chalk.

Put a dot where your finger was, at the center of the circle. Ask, **What is the name of this point?**

Label the dot *focus*. Tell students that other parts of a circle have names and that in this

Additional Information

Most students will recall that the center of a circle is called the *focus*. Acknowledge the correct answers.

activity they will learn those terms and how to measure and draw circles of different sizes.

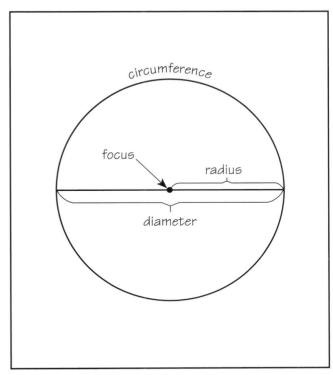

Figure 4-1. Parts of a circle.

Trace the curve of the circle on the board with your finger and ask, **Do you know what this part of the circle is called?**

Write *circumference* just outside the curve of the circle on the board.

Use the meterstick to draw a radius on the circle you have drawn on the board. Ask, **How could you measure the size of this circle?**

Label the line *radius.* Explain that a radius is the distance from the focus to the circumference of the circle. Use the string and chalk again to show them that the radius of this circle is the length of the string used to draw the circle.

Use the meterstick to show them that the radius can be measured in any direction from the focus to any point on the circumference of one circle and that each radius is the same length.

2 Some students will know that the closed curve of a circle is called the *circumference.*

Some students already understand the concepts of radius and diameter. Acknowledge any correct answers.

Tell students that next you will draw a smaller circle. Ask, **Do you think this circle will have a smaller or a larger radius than the first circle?**

Shorten the length of string and draw a smaller circle with chalk next to the first one. Explain that the length of the radius of a circle is one measure of the size of that circle.

smaller

3

Lay the meterstick along the radius of the first, larger circle. Extend the radius to draw a diameter. Ask, **Do you know what the name of this distance is?**

Some students may respond with the correct answer—diameter.

Label the *diameter* of the circle. Point out that a diameter is the distance from the circumference of the circle, through the focus, to the circumference on other side.

Draw several diameters from different points on the circumference. Show them that it does not matter where they draw a diameter in the circle; all the diameters will be the same length.

Ask, **Do you think the smaller circle has a smaller or larger diameter than the first circle?**

smaller

Explain that the diameter of a circle, like the radius, is one measure of the size of that circle.

4

Distribute a metric ruler and a cardboard square to each team and a copy of Activity Sheet 4 to each student.

Do not distribute the drawing compasses or sheets of plain paper yet.

Have students retrieve their *Circle and Ellipse* papers that they saved in Activity 3.

Tell students to answer the first two questions on Activity Sheet 4. Remind them to record their measurements.

Students are to measure the radius and diameter of the circles they drew in the previous activity. Remind them to measure only the circles, not the ellipses.

5

Hold up a drawing compass for the class to see and ask, **What do you think this instrument is called and what is it used for?**

Many students will not know what it is.

Write *drawing compass* on the board. Explain that a drawing compass is an instrument that can be used to draw a circle.

Demonstrate how to use a drawing compass to make a circle. Borrow a team's metric ruler and cardboard square. Tape a clean sheet of plain paper on the cardboard. Measure to find the approximate center point of the paper, make a dot with a pencil, and label the dot *C*.

First, tell students that you want to draw a circle with a radius of 5 cm (about 2 in.).

Show them how the arms of the drawing compass can be manipulated to spread or close the tips. Show them 5 cm on the ruler. Adjust the arms of the drawing compass until the distance from the metal point of the drawing compass to the pencil tip measures 5 cm. The instrument will maintain this measurement.

Tell students to ignore the measurement markings on the compass itself as these are often inaccurate.

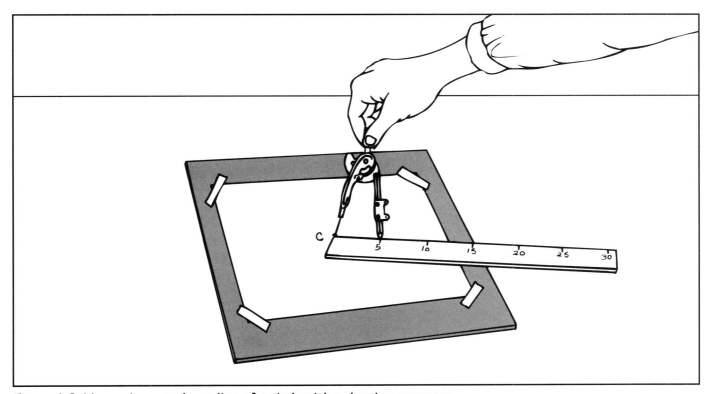

Figure 4-2. Measuring out the radius of a circle with a drawing compass.

Stick the metal point into the dot *C* on the paper, grasp the top of the drawing compass, and rotate the pencil arm to draw a circle on the paper.

Tell students that next they will use drawing compasses to draw their own circles. Return the team's metric ruler and cardboard square.

Distribute a drawing compass and two clean sheets of plain paper to each team. Show students where to get the masking tape. Tell students to complete Activity Sheet 4.

If any students have difficulty using the drawing compasses, show them how to hold the metal tip in place with one hand as they rotate the pencil tip in a circle.

After teams have finished measuring and drawing circles, lead a discussion about the sizes of the circles they drew. Ask, **What relationship did you notice between the radius and diameter of each circle?**

A radius is half the length of a diameter of any one circle (or a diameter is twice the length of a radius for any one circle).

Ask, **How did you change the size of your circles?**

by changing the length of the radius

Point out that as the size of the radius increased, so did the size of the circle drawn.

Ask, **If you wanted to draw a picture of a planet on a sheet of paper, what shape would you draw?**

a circle

Remind students that they learned in previous activities that the Sun and its satellites are shaped like huge balls of various sizes. Ask, **How could being able to draw different-sized circles help you represent different planets in the Solar System?**

Responses will vary somewhat, but most students will say that by drawing circles of different sizes they could represent planets of different sizes.

Tell students that in a later activity they will measure and draw circles of different sizes and then cut out the circles to make models of the planets in our Solar System.

Reinforcement

List three or four diameter measurements on the board. Have students use their drawing compasses to draw circles having those diameters. (Make the diameters whole even numbers so students can easily divide them by 2 to calculate the radii measurements.)

Cleanup

Have teams carefully remove their papers from the cardboard and discard the pieces of masking tape. Tell them to write their names on the papers and keep them together with their papers entitled *Circle* *and Ellipse.* Drawing compasses, cardboard squares, metric rulers, the meterstick, the roll of masking tape, and the ball of string should be returned to the kit.

Science at Home

Have students measure and list the diameters and radii of objects around their homes that have circular shapes, such as a lampshade, coat button, watch face, dinner plate, drinking cup, and so on.

Connections

Science Challenge

Tell students that one of the challenges facing the scientists who planned the Moon landings in the 1960s and 1970s was aiming the spacecraft so it would arrive at the Moon. Students can gain a basic understanding of this problem by doing the following activity in small groups: Tape one end of a 60-cm (2-ft) string to one end of a ruler, and tie a metal washer to the other end of the string. Lay the ruler on a desk with its end over the edge so the washer hangs freely, and put a book on the ruler to hold it in place. Make a supply of grape-size wads of paper toweling. Then one student should sit about 1 m (1 yd) from the washer, and another student should pull the washer to one side and let it go so it swings back and forth. The first student should try to hit the moving washer with a paper wad. Other team members should then take their turns. Ask students to explain why it was so difficult to hit the washer at first and what they had to do in order to improve their results. (The wad must be aimed in front of the washer so both objects arrive at the same place at the same time.)

Science Extension

Ask the "Earth" team to report additional information they have found and to record Earth's data on the class master chart.

Additional Facts About Earth
Volume: 1
Mass: 1
Density (water = 1): 5.52
Surface temperature: –94°F to +130°F
   (–70°C to +55°C)
Composition: solid iron inner core, molten
   iron outer core, rocky mantle, rocky crust
Distinctive features: only planet known to
   support life; unique combination of
   abundant water and oxygen/nitrogen-
   based atmosphere

Additional Facts About Earth's Moon
Volume (Earth = 1): 0.02
Mass (Earth = 1): 0.012
Density (water = 1): 3.34
Surface temperature: –230°F to +220°F
   (–145°C to +105°C)
Composition: core (perhaps iron), partially
   molten region, rocky mantle
Distinctive features: no atmosphere, so no
   surface weathering; same side always
   faces Earth

Science and Social Studies

Since ancient times, people have studied the objects in the sky, using their observations to tell time, create calendars, plan seasonal activities such as planting and harvesting crops, and direct religious ceremonies. Encourage interested students to find out about ancient observatories and other structures used to track celestial patterns. Such structures include the world's oldest observatory, Chomsung dae, in Kyongju, Korea; Stonehenge in England; Mayan pyramids in Central America; and "America's Stonehenge" in Salisbury, New Hampshire. If any students have visited the New Hampshire site, ask them to describe the structure.

Science, Technology, and Society

Provide books containing photographs of Earth taken from space. One excellent source is *Seeing Earth from Space* by Patricia Lauber (Orchard Books, 1990), which includes unusual satellite photographs produced with infrared, radar, and false-color imaging as well as spectacular NASA photographs of the entire planet and various surface features. If students get cable television that includes a NASA channel, they may be able to see live broadcasts showing Earth from an orbiting satellite. Give students an opportunity to describe their reactions to all these images.

Activity 5
Scale and Relative Size

Objectives

In this activity students explore the concept of scale and find that scale drawings can help them determine both the relative and the actual sizes of objects.

The students

■ explore the relationships among metric units of measure

■ calculate actual heights of objects drawn to scale

■ determine relative size using scale drawings of familiar objects

■ discover that drawings of objects must be made to the same scale in order to determine their relative sizes

Schedule

About 50 minutes

Vocabulary

centimeter (cm)	relative size
meter (m)	scale
millimeter (mm)	scale drawing
ratio	

Materials

For each student
1   Activity Sheet 5

For each team of two
2 sht   *paper, plain
1   ruler, metric

For the class
8   metersticks
1   poster, Goldfish and Whale scale drawing
1   *map

*provided by the teacher

Preparation

1. Make a copy of Activity Sheet 5 for each student.

2. Each team of two will need a metric ruler and two sheets of plain paper. Have each team share a meterstick with another team.

3. Do not display the Goldfish and Whale scale drawing poster until instructed to do so later in the activity.

Background Information

The sizes of the Sun and planets in our Solar System are huge almost beyond comprehension. Scale drawings (or models) can, however, represent these objects so that students can visualize and compare them. In a scale drawing, objects can be greatly reduced in size but still remain in proportion to one another.

Scale is a proportion, or a *ratio*, between two sets of dimensions—as between those of a drawing (or a model) and those of the original object. For example, if a drawing of a bicycle were made to a scale of 1 cm to 20 cm, its scale would be written as 1:20, spoken of as "1 to 20." One unit of measure in the drawing would represent 20 units of the same measure in the bicycle.

If the units of measurement in the ratio are different—centimeters compared to kilometers, for example—the scale is written somewhat differently. For example, if 1 cm on a map represents 10 km in actual distance, the map's scale is 1 cm:10 km and is spoken of as "1 centimeter to 10 kilometers."

Scale drawings can be used to determine and to visualize *relative size*—the size of one object compared to that of another. However, in order to portray accurately the relative sizes of two objects, their drawings must be made to the same scale.

In subsequent activities, students will apply what they learn in this activity about scale drawings and relative size to construct a scale model of the Solar System.

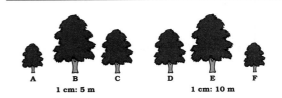

Scale and Relative Size

A   B   C   D   E   F
1 cm: 5 m   1 cm: 10 m

Measure the height of each drawing of a tree. Record your measurement of the drawing in the chart below. Then calculate the heights of the actual trees.

	Tree A	Tree B	Tree C	Tree D	Tree E	Tree F
Drawing Height (cm)	2	4	3	3	4	2
Actual Height (m)	10	20	15	30	40	20

What is the scale used to draw Trees A, B, and C? 1 cm:5 m

What is the scale used to draw Trees D, E, and F? 1 cm:10 m

Is the drawing of Tree A the same height as the drawing of Tree F? Yes.

Is the actual height of Tree A the same as the actual height of Tree F? Why or why not?

No, because the scales are different.

If the drawings are the same heights, but the scales to which they were drawn are different, are the actual heights of the trees the same or different? different

How could you tell which actual tree is taller if you have two drawings that are the same heights but have been drawn to different scales? (Hint: Compare the scale ratios.)

The scale ratio with the largest second number will indicate which actual tree is taller.

Teaching Suggestions

1

Distribute a metric ruler to each team of two. Have students find the smallest divisions on the rulers. Write *millimeter* and *mm* on the board.

Explain that these small marks are measurements called millimeters and are abbreviated *mm*. Tell students to count 10 of the millimeter marks starting from the zero end of the ruler.

Ask, **What number is written by the mark at 10 millimeters?**

Write *centimeter* and *cm* on the board. Explain that 10 millimeters is equal in length to 1 centimeter. Ask, **How many centimeters long is your ruler?**

Tell students that you have another type of ruler for them to examine. Pair up each team with another team. Distribute a meterstick to each pair of teams.

Additional Information

the numeral 1

30.5

2

Four students will share one meterstick.

Write *meter* and *m* on the board. Explain that a meterstick is 1 meter long and that meter is abbreviated *m*.

Ask, **If this meterstick is 1 meter long, how long is it in centimeters?**

Some students may wish to measure it with their metric rulers. Acknowledge correct answers: The meterstick is 100 centimeters long; or 1 meter is equal to 100 centimeters.

Ask, **If 1 meter is equal to 100 centimeters, how many millimeters are there in 1 meter?**

There are 1000 millimeters in 1 meter.

Continue to explore the relationships among millimeter, centimeter, and meter until students are familiar with the measurements.

Ask, **Thirty millimeters equals how many centimeters? Four centimeters equals how many millimeters? One meter equals how many centimeters?**

3 centimeters
40 millimeters
100 centimeters

Write the words *scale* and *ratio* on the board. Explain that scale is a way of showing the size of one object in proportion to another larger or smaller object—that is, how the size of one object is related to the size of another. A numerical *ratio* is used to express scale.

3

Write *1:30* on the board. Tell students a scale represented by a ratio such as "1 to 30" means that 1 unit of measure in the smaller object represents 30 units in the larger object.

Use a team's meterstick to draw a 1-cm line on the board. Ask, **If this line is a scale drawing of the meterstick, what is the scale of the drawing?**

Help students to conclude that since 1 centimeter on the board represents 100 centimeters (1 meter) in the actual object, the scale is 1:100.

Write *1:100* on the board beneath the 1-cm line.

Draw on the board a tree that is about 60 cm (about 2 ft) tall. Underneath the drawing of the tree write the ratio *1:30* (see Figure 5-1).

4

Do not let students see you measure the 60 cm.

Ask, **What is the scale of this drawing?**

1 to 30

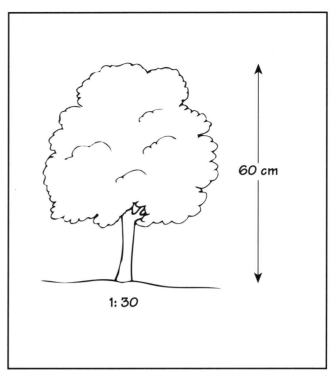

Figure 5-1. A scale drawing.

Tell students to imagine that this image represents an actual tree outside. Ask, **How can we find out how tall the actual tree is?**

Explain that to determine the height of the actual tree from the scale drawing, students must know both the height of the drawing and the scale at which the tree is drawn.

Let students see you measure the height of the drawing. Tell students that the height of the drawing is 60 cm. Write *60 cm* to one side of the drawing.

Point to the ratio under the drawing. Remind students that this ratio means that every 1 cm of height in the drawing represents 30 cm in the height of the actual tree.

Ask, **How tall is the actual tree that this drawing represents?**

Explain that the height of the actual tree is determined by multiplying 60 cm by 30 cm —1800 cm.

Ask, **How tall do you think that the actual tree is in meters?**

Encourage answers that take into account measuring the height of the drawing and using the scale 1:30.

Acknowledge any correct responses. The actual tree is 1800 cm (about 59 ft) tall.

Acknowledge correct answers: 1800 divided by 100 equals 18 m.

Distribute a copy of Activity Sheet 5 to each student. Tell students to measure the drawings of trees at the top of the page and use the scale under the drawings to determine the heights of the actual trees. Tell them to record the information in the chart on their activity sheets and answer the questions below the chart.

After teams have completed Activity Sheet 5, ask, **At the scale of 1 cm to 5 m, which drawing is largest? Which is smallest?**

The drawing of Tree B is largest and that of Tree A is smallest.

Then ask, **At the scale of 1 cm to 10 m, which drawing is largest? Which is smallest?**

The drawing of Tree E is largest and that of Tree F is smallest.

Tell students to look at the drawings of Tree C and Tree D on their activity sheets. Ask, **Would you be able to determine which actual tree is larger, Tree C or Tree D, if you did not know the scale?**

No. The drawings are the same size.

Ask, **How could you determine which drawing represents the larger real-life tree if you examine two scale drawings that are the same size but the ratios in the scales are different?**

If the second number in the ratio is higher, the scale represents a taller actual tree.

Write the term *relative size* on the board and explain that relative size means how large (or small) one object is when compared to the size of another object.

Call students' attention to Trees A, B, and C, all of which are drawn to the same scale. Ask, **Which tree do you think is larger in relative size, Tree A or Tree B?**

If necessary, remind students to compare the sizes of the two drawings and determine which is larger. Tree B is larger relative to the size of Tree A.

Ask, **Do you think that the actual size of Tree B is also larger than the actual size of Tree A? How can you tell?**

Yes, because they are drawn to the same scale.

Point out to students that in order to determine the relative sizes (or the actual sizes) of two or more objects based on their drawings, the drawings must be done according to the same scale.

To emphasize this point, distribute two sheets of plain notebook paper to each team of two. Tell one student in each team to draw a goldfish on his or her sheet of paper and the other student to draw a whale.

When they have finished, have them compare the two drawings. Ask, **Can you determine the relative sizes of these two animals by comparing their relative sizes in your drawings?**

Students will say they cannot determine the relative sizes because the drawings were not drawn to the same scale. The whale obviously had to be scaled down considerably to fit on the paper. Chances are that students did not reduce the size of the goldfish to the same degree.

Display the Goldfish and Whale scale drawing poster. Have students compare these images with their drawings. Point out that the drawings you are showing them can be used to determine the relative sizes of the two animals because they are drawn to the same scale.

10

The scale is 1:20.

Ask, **What has this exercise taught you about the usefulness of scale drawings for determining the relative sizes of objects?**

Students should respond that scale drawings are helpful for comparing relative sizes only if they are made according to the same scale.

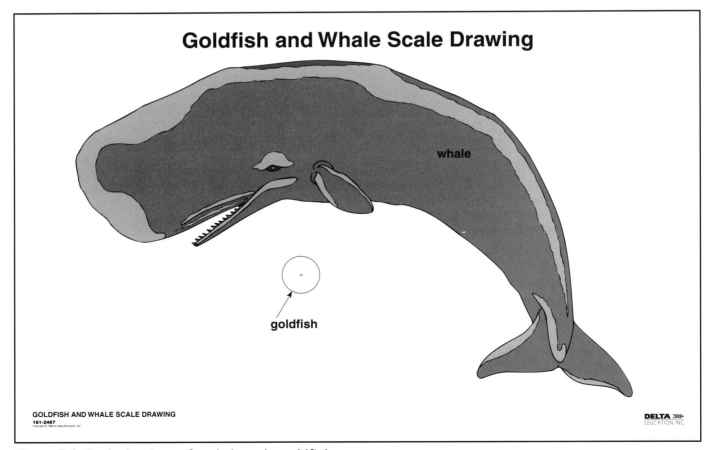

Goldfish and Whale Scale Drawing

whale

goldfish

GOLDFISH AND WHALE SCALE DRAWING
161-2467
Copyright © 1996 by Delta Education, Inc.

DELTA ≫
EDUCATION, INC.

Figure 5-2. Scale drawings of a whale and a goldfish.

Reinforcement

Obtain a scale model toy—a car, boat, train, or doll, for example—to show the class. Find out the scale to which the model was made and have students calculate the dimensions of the actual object based on that scale.

Cleanup

Have students return the metric rulers and metersticks to the kit. They may keep their animal drawings or discard them, as they wish. The scale drawings poster of the goldfish and the whale should be returned to the kit.

Science at Home

Students can explore scale and relative size of towns and counties shaded in different colors on a local map at home.

Connections

Science Extension

Ask the "Mars" team to report additional information they have found and to record Mars's data on the class master chart.

Additional Facts About Mars
Volume (Earth = 1): 0.15
Mass (Earth = 1): 0.11
Density (water = 1): 3.95
Surface temperature: –185°F to +77°F (–120°C to +25°C)
Composition: solid iron core, rocky mantle, solid crust
Names of moons: Phobos, Deimos
Distinctive features: Earthlike seasons; polar ice caps made of frozen water and carbon dioxide; largest volcano in the Solar System (Olympus Mons); called the "Red Planet" because of iron-rich, reddish dust covering the surface

As a preliminary to making scale models of the Sun and planets in Activity 6, teams of students could make a simple model to show the relative sizes of the Sun, Earth, and Moon, as follows: On a large sheet of newsprint or brown packaging paper, draw a circle with a diameter of 105 cm (3.5 ft) to represent the Sun. Just inside the large circle, draw another circle with a diameter of 1 cm to represent Earth. Near this circle draw another circle with a diameter of 2.5 mm (0.1 in.) to represent the Moon. Color the Earth circle blue and the Moon circle black. The impact of these relative sizes will be dramatic if each team tapes its drawing to a wall and views it from a distance.

Science and Language Arts

The July 25, 1994 issue of *Newsweek* contains a cover story titled "Next Stop Mars" with the intriguing question, "Scientists can get us there, but do we dare?" If your students are capable of understanding the adult language level of the article, read it aloud to the class or provide copies for them to read on their own. Follow up the reading with a discussion of the pros and cons of a manned mission to Mars. Then ask two groups of volunteers to stage a debate on whether such a mission is worth the huge investment of money, time, and effort that it would require.

Ask students to suggest other meanings of the word *scale*—a device used to weigh things; a sequence of musical tones; a small, hard, platelike structure forming the outer covering of fish and reptiles; and to climb up something, such as a cliff. If students cannot think of these other meanings on their own, ask them to consult a dictionary.

Science and Math

In Activity 6 students will use the diameters of the Sun and planets and a given ratio to calculate the sizes of scale models. The following activity involves using only the diameters to calculate the relative sizes of the Sun and planets compared with Earth. For the Sun and the planets that are larger than Earth, have students divide the larger body's diameter by Earth's diameter. For planets smaller than Earth, have them divide Earth's diameter by the smaller planet's diameter. Let students use calculators to determine the exact relative sizes and then describe them in the following "rounded off" terms.

Sun and larger planets. The Sun is 109 times larger, Jupiter about 11 times larger, Saturn almost 9.5 times larger, and Uranus and Neptune about 4 times larger than Earth.

Smaller planets. Earth is more than 5 times larger than Pluto, about 2.5 times larger than Mercury, almost 2 times larger than Mars, and slightly (1.05 times) larger than Venus.

Activity 6
Modeling Planet Sizes

Objectives

In this activity, students apply what they have learned about circles and scale to make scale models of the planets.

The students
- calculate the radii for scale models of the planets
- make a scale model of each planet
- compare the relative sizes of the planets

Schedule

About 40 minutes

Materials

For each student

1	Activity Sheet 6

For each team of two

1	cardboard, square
1	compass, drawing
1	*marker, black
1 sht	paper, construction, black
1	ruler, metric
1 pair	*scissors

For the class

1	*BB
1	*baseball
1	*basketball
1	*marble
1 sht	paper, construction, blue
1 roll	masking tape

*provided by the teacher

Preparation

1. Make a copy of Activity Sheet 6 for each student.

2. Cut the sheet of blue construction paper into sixteen 5-cm (about 2-in.) squares, one for each team.

3. Each team of two will need a metric ruler, a drawing compass, a cardboard square, one sheet of black construction paper, a 5-cm square of blue construction paper, a pair of scissors, a black marker, and access to the masking tape.

Background Information

The enormity of the objects that make up our Solar System is difficult to imagine. The diameter of the Sun (the largest object in our Solar System) is 1,392,000 km. The diameter of Pluto (the smallest planet) is 2,400 km, while that of Jupiter (the largest planet) is 143,200 km.

To create a model of our Solar System on a classroom wall so that students can visualize the relative sizes of the Sun and the planets requires the use of a scale. A scale of 1 cm:5,000 km makes Pluto about 0.5 cm (about 0.2 in.) in diameter and Jupiter about 28.6 cm (about 11.25 in.) in diameter.

Although a comparison of numerical measurements of the planets' diameters reveals their relative sizes directly, a visual representation is far more impressive. Even though students may know that Jupiter is

59 times larger than Pluto, they will be astonished to see on a scale model the contrast between a dot of less than 0.5 cm in diameter to a circle almost 29 cm in diameter.

Modeling Planet Sizes

How can you make models of the planets that allow you to compare their relative sizes? Reduce the actual diameter of the planets according to the same ratio, draw circles using the scaled radii, and compare the size of the circles.

Name	Actual Diameter (km)	Scale Model Diameter (cm) Scale = 1 cm:5000 km	Scale Model Radius (cm) Scale = 1 cm:5000 km
Sun	1,392,000	278.4	139.2
Mercury	4,878	1.0	0.5
Venus	12,100	2.4	1.2
Earth	12,756	2.6	1.3
Mars	6,786	1.4	0.7
Jupiter	143,200	28.6	14.3
Saturn	120,536	24.1	12.1
Uranus	51,118	10.2	5.1
Neptune	49,528	9.9	5.0
Pluto	2,400	0.5	0.3

1. Calculate each scale model radius from the scale model diameters given above. Record the radius in the Scale Model Radius column.

2. Use the Scale Model Radius measurements to measure, draw, and cut out circles. The circles representing Mercury, Mars, and Pluto will be too small to measure with the drawing compass. Use the ruler to measure these three planets and draw the circles by hand.

3. Write the names of the four largest planets on strips of masking tape with the black marker and then attach the labels to those models. Make tape "handles" for the five smallest planets, as shown on the board. Write their names on the tape handles.

List the planets according to relative size. Start with the largest and finish with the smallest.

Jupiter, Saturn, Uranus, Neptune, Earth, Venus, Mars, Mercury, and Pluto

Teaching Suggestions

1

Ask students to review the concept of relative size. Show them the basketball, baseball, marble, and BB. Discuss the size of each object relative to the others.

Ask, **How do you think the Sun and the planets compare with one another in size?**

2

Review the concept of *scale* and why scale drawings are useful. Remind students of how they used scale drawings in the previous activity to visualize the relative sizes of actual objects. Ask, **What is one way we can investigate the relative sizes of the planets?**

Remind students that a planet's shape is similar to that of a ball. Ask, **In Activity 4, what shape did you decide you would draw to represent a ball? What measurement would you need in order to make a scale drawing of this shape?**

Additional Information

Accept all responses.

Students may suggest making scale drawings of the planets and placing them side by side to compare their sizes.

a circle; the diameter or the radius of the circle

Explain to students that in this activity they will make scale drawings of the planets and then cut them out and line them up so that they can visualize and compare their sizes.

Review the names of all of the planets in our Solar System. Ask students to name them in order of their distance from the Sun. Suggest they use the mnemonic devices they learned in Activity 1, if necessary.

3 Mercury, Venus, Earth, Mars, Jupiter, Saturn, Uranus, Neptune, Pluto

Choose, or have a student volunteer choose, a planet. Write the planet's name on the board. Refer to the chart in Figure 6-1 and write the planet's actual diameter to the right of its name.

Ask, **Can you make your model the same size as the actual planet?**

No. The planet is much too big!

Explain that they will make scale models of the planets that are much smaller than the actual planets.

Although technically a scale model reflects all three dimensions of the actual object, we will refer to the cut-out scale drawings as "scale models" in this activity.

Remind students that they know that Pluto, for example, is tiny compared to Jupiter. Ask, **Could you use a different scale for each model planet to show their relative sizes?**

No. To show their relative sizes accurately, the same scale must be used for all the model planets.

Name	Actual Diameter (km)	Scale Model Diameter (cm) Scale = 1 cm:5000 km	Scale Model Radius (cm) Scale = 1 cm:5000 km
Sun	1,392,000	278.4	139.2
Mercury	4,878	1.0	0.5
Venus	12,100	2.4	1.2
Earth	12,756	2.6	1.3
Mars	6,786	1.4	0.7
Jupiter	143,200	28.6	14.3
Saturn	120,536	24.1	12.1
Uranus	51,118	10.2	5.1
Neptune	49,528	9.9	5.0
Pluto	2,400	0.5	0.3

Figure 6-1. Planet diameters, actual and scaled.

Tell students the scale for the classroom models is 1 cm to 5,000 km. Above the name and diameter of the planet already written on the board, write *1 cm:5,000 km.*

Write the scaled diameter for the planet on the board to the right of the actual diameter.

4

Ask, **If this is the diameter of your planet model, how would you calculate the radius?**

divide the diameter by 2

Ask, **What is the radius of this scale model?**

Have students calculate and call out the radius of the scale model.

Write the scaled radius on the board to the right of the scaled diameter. Tell students that to create a scale model of this planet they will draw a circle of this radius on construction paper and cut out the circle. Next, they will write the name of the planet on a strip of masking tape with a black marker and place the strip on the model planet.

Tell students they will use this same scale (1 cm: 5,000 km) to make a model of each planet.

Distribute a copy of Activity Sheet 6 to each student. Tell students to read the question at the top of the activity sheet and write the answer.

5

Give students a few minutes to answer the question, and then ask several volunteers to read their answers. Acknowledge correct answers and discuss them to ensure that all students understand the reasoning behind the procedure.

Call students' attention to the chart on the activity sheet. Have them locate the columns headed *Actual Diameter, Scale Model Diameter,* and *Scale Model Radius.* Tell students to calculate and write down the measurements for the scale model radii in the right-hand column. Remind them to round their answers to the nearest tenth of a centimeter (1 mm).

Tell them to skip the Sun for the present and to write scaled radii for only the nine planets. They will scale the Sun's diameter and radius at the end of the activity.

Give students a few minutes to calculate the scaled radii and write them on the chart. Then have a volunteer from each team name a planet (except the one on the board) and give its scaled radius, beginning with

Mercury and ending with Pluto. After each answer, ask, **Do you all agree with that scaled radius measurement?**

As students reach consensus on the scaled radius of each planet, write the planet's name and its scaled radius on the board.

If students do not all agree, ask a volunteer who has a different answer for his or her calculation. If necessary, do the calculation on the board.

Conforming the scaled radii measurements on all the activity sheets will help ensure that all students' planet models will be the correct sizes.

Distribute to each team of two the metric rulers, scissors, drawing compasses, cardboard squares, sheet of black construction paper, squares of blue construction paper, and black markers. Have the roll of masking tape available.

Tell students to use the square of blue construction paper to make the model of Earth and to use the black construction paper to make models of the other planets.

Remind them that to make a model of a planet they need to place the construction paper on the cardboard, measure with the metric ruler the scale model radius of the planet, set the drawing compass to the scaled radius, draw a circle on the paper, and cut out the circle.

Suggest they draw the larger planets first, close to the corners of the black construction paper. Tell them to make a practice swing around with their drawing compasses to make sure the circle will not go off the edge of the paper.

Tell students the scaled radii of Mercury, Venus, Earth, Mars, and Pluto are too small to be measured with the drawing compass. Have students measure the scaled diameters of these five planets with their metric rulers and hand-draw the circles.

Tell them to stick each of the five small models to one end of a piece of masking tape and to fold the other end back on itself, sticky sides together. Tell students to write the name of the planet on the tape "handle" with a black marker. Refer to Figure 6-2 and draw an example on the board.

Tell students to write the names of the four largest planets on strips of masking tape with the black marker and then attach the labels to their models.

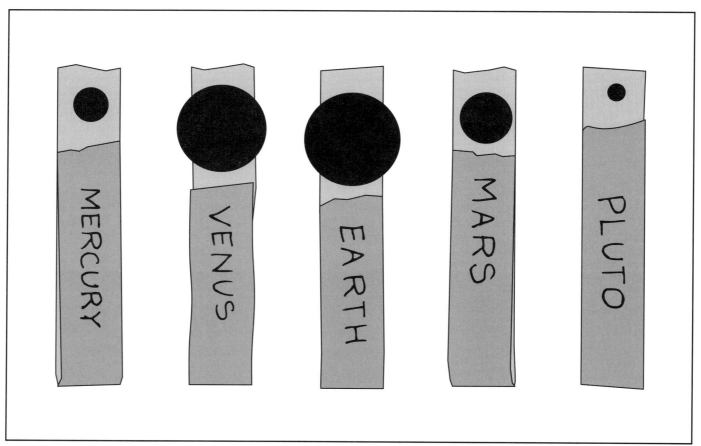

Figure 6-2. Labeling the five smallest planets.

After teams have finished making their models, have them arrange their planet models side by side in the same order that the planets appear relative to the Sun. (The display will be about 90 cm [about 35 in.] long.)

7

Students may refer to Activity Sheet 1 or use their mnemonic devices to recall the order of the planets relative to the Sun.

Ask, **Judging from your models, which planet is larger than Saturn?**

Jupiter

By looking at your scale models, what else can you tell about the relative sizes of the planets?

Answers will vary. Most students will note that Jupiter and Saturn are much bigger than the other planets and that Pluto is tiny. Some will say that Earth is relatively small compared with the others.

Have students locate the actual diameter measurements for Saturn and Jupiter on Activity Sheet 6. Ask, **What do these measurements tell you about the relative sizes of the actual planets?**

Jupiter is larger than Saturn.

Ask, **What can you determine about the relative sizes of the planets by considering their diameters?**

Answers will vary. Most students will say that the planets are all different sizes, some smaller and some larger than others.

Ask, **Why do we not just compare their diameter measurements on the chart to visualize their relative sizes?**

Most students will respond that they can visualize the relative sizes of the planets better by looking at a model than they can by comparing numbers on a chart.

Explain that although measurements of actual diameters can be compared to determine relative size directly, a model drawn to scale can give us a clearer and more vivid mental picture of the enormous differences in size among the planets.

Reinforcement

Ask students to find the Sun and its actual diameter in the chart on Activity Sheet 6. Have them calculate and write in the chart the scale model diameter and radius to the same scale as the planets (1 cm:5,000 km). (The actual diameter of the Sun is 1,392,000 km; its scaled diameter is 278.4 cm; therefore, its scaled radius is 139.2 cm.)

Cleanup

Have students return the drawing compasses, metric rulers, and cardboard squares to the kit. Have them discard the scraps of paper left from cutting out their models. The roll of masking tape should be returned to the kit. Have teams store their scale models in a safe place.

Connections

Science Challenge

Ask students to name different scale models with which they are familiar. After they have named the most obvious types—cars, railroads, and the like—prompt them to identify scale models they may have made or used in science or social studies classes. A map, for example, is a scale model. Emphasize that not all models are smaller than the actual objects. Ask students if they know of any models that are larger than the objects they represent. They may cite models of molecules or cells.

Science Extension

Ask the "Jupiter" team to report additional information they have found and to record Jupiter's data on the class master chart.

Additional Facts About Jupiter
Volume (Earth = 1): 1,319
Mass (Earth = 1): 318
Density (water = 1): 1.33
Temperature at cloud tops: –240°F (–150°C)
Composition: small rocky core, liquid and
    gaseous hydrogen and helium
Names of major moons: Io, Callisto, Europa,
    Ganymede
Distinctive features: largest planet in the
    Solar System, larger than all other
    planets combined; gas clouds create dark
    belts and bright zones; Great Red Spot
    believed to be giant storm; thin ring, not
    visible from Earth, discovered by
    Voyager 1 in 1979

Ask students to bring in scale models that they or their family members have built, along with the box or instructions identifying the models' scales. Let students compare the models to see that different scales result in different size models. For example, a 1:20 scale model will be much smaller than a 1:10 scale model of the same object. A 1:10 model of a car may be as large or larger than a 1:20 scale model of a truck. Have students group together all the models designed to the same scale. Ask them whether the real objects would be the same relative sizes. (yes) Also explain that a model's scale applies to all its dimensions, not just length. Have each student measure different dimensions on a model—width, height, length of one part, and so on—and use the model's scale to calculate those dimensions on the real object.

Science and Math

If your students have had limited practice with decimals, explain the scale measurements on Activity Sheet 6 in simple terms: The number before the decimal gives centimeters and the number after the decimal gives millimeters, just as dollars and cents are written in our money system.

Science, Technology, and Society

Tell students that in 1989, a space probe named *Galileo*—in honor of the scientist they researched in Science and Social Studies for Activity 2—was launched to Jupiter. Unlike the *Voyager* probes, which flew past Jupiter, *Galileo* was designed to go into orbit around the planet. In July 1995, *Galileo* released a small probe designed to plunge toward Jupiter and reach its atmosphere in December 1995. Before the small probe is destroyed by the atmosphere's high temperatures and pressure, it is expected to radio information about the atmosphere back to the *Galileo* orbiter, which will relay the data to scientists on Earth. Encourage interested students to find updated information about the *Galileo* probe and orbiter.

Activity 7

Scale and Relative Distance

Objectives

In this activity, students apply what they have learned about scale to relative distance. They discover that scale drawings can help them visualize the relative distances of objects from one another in space.

The students

■ relate the concept of relative size to relative distance

■ calculate distances on a map using scaled distance data

■ create a scale drawing from actual distance measurements

Schedule

About 40 minutes

Vocabulary

map
relative distance

Materials

For each student
1   Activity Sheet 7

For each team of four
1   meterstick
1   ruler, metric

For the class
1   *map, local

*provided by the teacher

Preparation

1. Make a copy of Activity Sheet 7 for each student.

2. Copy on the board the simple map shown in Figure 7-1. Measure and draw the lines, representing streets, 30 cm apart. Label the three locations *School, Home,* and *Store,* as shown in the figure. Write the scale *15 cm:1 km* below the map.

3. Each team of four will need a metric ruler and a meterstick.

Background Information

In addition to being used to make drawings that accurately represent relative size, scale can be used to make drawings that accurately represent relative distance. The most common example is a map—a scale drawing of an actual geographic area that marks the locations of points of interest and accurately represents the relative distance between different sets of objects.

Not all maps or charts are drawn to the same scale. City maps are drawn to depict greater detail than are state or United States maps. The scale for city maps is often 1 cm:2 km, whereas the scale for many United States maps is 1 cm:100 km. These very different scales are necessary to reduce the drawing of a very large area, such as the continental United States, to fit on a single sheet of paper.

In this activity, students will become familiar with "reading" a map—using scaled distances on a map to calculate actual distances. Then they will measure the actual distance between objects in the classroom, reduce the measurements to a common scale, and make a scale drawing that shows the relative distances of those objects from one another.

Teaching Suggestions

Additional Information

1

Review students' use of scale in constructing models of a set of objects to show accurately their relative sizes.

2

Write the term *relative distance* on the board. Explain that relative distance means how far apart one set of objects are when compared with another set of objects.

Ask, **Can you name anything that shows relative distance and that is drawn to scale?**

Most students will be familiar with maps, and some of them may have seen nautical charts. Architectural drawings and blueprints are also scale drawings that show both relative size and distance.

Show students a local map. Explain that a *map* is a scale drawing. Maps are used to represent the geographic location of places and things. Maps also show the relative distances between different locations on the map.

Tell students that they will first learn how to read actual distances on a map by using a

scale. Then they will measure actual
distances in the classroom and make their
own scale drawing.

Bring students' attention to the simple map
you have drawn on the board.

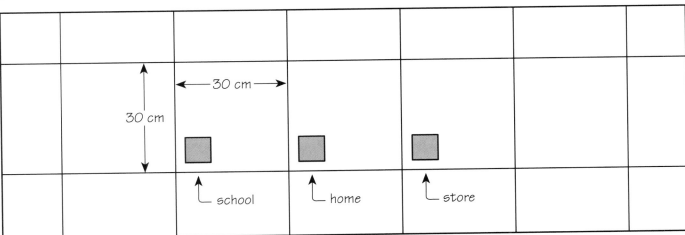

Figure 7-1. A simple neighborhood map.

Ask, **To what scale has this map been
drawn?**

The correct response is "15 centimeters to
1 kilometer."

Explain the scale by telling students that
15 centimeters on the map represents
1 kilometer of actual distance.

Lay a meterstick against the board so that
students can see you measure the distance
between school and home. Ask, **What is the
scaled distance from school to home?
From school to the store?**

You may need to call out that the distances are
30 cm and 60 cm.

Ask, **According to the scale on this map,
how far is the actual distance from
school to home? From school to the
store?**

2 km; 4 km

**Which location is farther from school,
relative to the other location?**

the store

**Which location is closer to school,
relative to the other location?**

home

If students have difficulty with the concept
of relative distance, add two more buildings
to the map on the board and ask, **Now
which location is the farthest from
school, relative to the other locations?
Which is the closest?**

Answers will vary according to the locations of the
items you have added to the map.

Tell students that in this activity they will use what they know about scale to make a scale drawing that shows the relative distances of a group of objects from one another.

Place a book on the floor in front of the board.

The purpose of the book is simply to have all teams measure from the same object. In the next activity, students will use measurements made from the Sun out to each planet.

Explain that students will measure the distances from the book to their desks, from the book to your desk, and from the book to the wall opposite the book. They are then to decide on a scale and make a scale drawing of these distances on their activity sheets.

Students should measure the straight line connecting each of these sets of points.

Give a copy of Activity Sheet 7 to each student. Distribute a metric ruler and a meterstick to each team of four.

Tell teams to follow the instructions on their activity sheets. They will measure straight line distances in the room, decide on a scale that will allow the scaled distances to fit on their activity sheets, and then make drawings on their activity sheets that represent the objects and show the scaled distances from one to another.

Depending on the level of your students, you may choose to do this exercise as a class, using a single scale decided on by all.

Suggest they decide on a scale by taking the longest distance first and scaling it down to fit in the space on the activity sheet.

After teams have completed Activity Sheet 7, begin a discussion of scale and relative distance.

Ask, **Which object is farthest from the board, relative to the other objects?**

the wall opposite the board

Tell students to examine their scale drawings and to imagine that they do not know the actual distances involved. Ask, **By looking at your scale drawing, can you make a good estimate of the relative distances of the objects from the board?**

Yes.

Explain that maps drawn accurately to scale allow us to visualize relative distances among points without having to calculate actual distances.

Ask, **How can this information be useful?**

Responses will vary. Some students may have found looking at maps useful during trips by car or plane.

Explain that a road map or a nautical chart helps us visualize and compare distances that separate points of interest. The relative distances shown on an architectural drawing or blueprint help us compare spaces on the inside or the outside of a building.

Tell students that scale drawings can also show the relative distances of the planets from the Sun. Explain that, in the next activity, students will look at the relative distances of the planets from the Sun.

Figure 7-2. Measuring distance on a map.

Reinforcement

On a city map, find and circle with a pencil a central landmark, such as a park or the city hall. Mark with *A, B, C, D,* and so on, several other places on the map at various distances from the central location. Ask students to describe the relative distances of the lettered spots from the central location. Then have them use the map scale and rulers (United States or metric, depending on the scale) to calculate the actual straight-line distance from the central location to the lettered locations.

Cleanup

Have students return the metersticks and the metric rulers to the kit.

Connections

Science Challenge

Take the class to a large room such as the cafeteria, auditorium, or gym. Have teams measure and record the distances of various objects from one wall of the room, as they did in the classroom for Activity Sheet 7. Back in the classroom, tell the teams that they are to make a scale drawing of the large room that is approximately the same size as their scale drawing of the classroom on the activity sheet. Challenge them to determine an appropriate scale on their own.

Science Extension

Ask the "Saturn" team to report additional information they have found and to record Saturn's data on the class master chart.

Additional Facts About Saturn
Volume (Earth = 1): 744
Mass (Earth = 1): 95.18
Density (water = 1): 0.69
Temperature at cloud tops: –292°F (–180°C)
Composition: rocky core, liquid hydrogen layer, metallic hydrogen layer
Names of major moons: Titan, Iapetus, Phoebe, Enceladus, Mimas, Tethys, Hyperion, Calypso; four new moons discovered May 1995 by astronomer Amanda Bosh using the Hubble telescope
Distinctive features: rings composed mostly of ice chunks; tilt of rings varies as seen from Earth

Science and Math

Have students use Earth's and the other planets' distances from the Sun (from Activity Sheet 8) to calculate each planet's distance from Earth, as follows: For the two planets closer to the Sun, subtract the planet's distance to the Sun from Earth's distance to the Sun. For the planets farther from the Sun, subtract Earth's distance from the planet's distance. You may want to have students perform the calculations with decimal figures—149.6 million km for Earth, for example—rather than the full figures with multiple zeroes.

Distance from Earth
Mercury: 91,800,000 (91.8 million) km
Venus: 41,400,000 (41.4 million) km
Mars: 78,300,000 (78.3 million) km
Jupiter: 628,700,000 (628.7 million) km
Saturn: 1,279,800,000 (1,279.8 million) km
Uranus: 2,721,400,000 (2,721.4 million) km
Neptune: 4,351,600,000 (4,351.6 million) km
Pluto: 5,850,400,000 (5,850.4 million) km

As an extension of the above activity, have students compare various distances by asking them questions such as: Which is greater—the distance from Mercury to the Sun or the distance from Mercury to Earth? (Mercury to the Earth) Which distance is greater—Venus to the Sun or Venus to Earth? (Venus to Sun) Which planet is closer to Earth—Mars or Venus? (Venus) Which is farther away from Earth—the Sun or Jupiter? (Jupiter)

Science and Social Studies

Give each student or team a copy of a road map of your town, area, or state. Have students measure the distance between two points—for example, the school and each student's own home—and use the map's scale to calculate the actual distance. For example, if the distance on the map is 3 inches and the map scale is 1.5 inches: 1 mile, the actual distance is 2 miles. Continue with other pairs of points. For each pair, you could have students measure both the straight-line ("as the crow flies") distance and the distance by road. To measure the distance by road, students can lay a string along the route from point A to point B and then stretch the string taut along a ruler.

Activity 8
Modeling Planet Distances

Objectives

Students apply what they have learned about scale and relative distance to build a model that helps them visualize the relative distances of the planets from the Sun.

The students

- discuss which scale would be appropriate for modeling the Solar System in the classroom

- make and display a model of the Solar System that shows the relative distances of the planets from the Sun

- compare distances of the various planets from the Sun

Schedule

About 50 minutes

Vocabulary

average distance

Materials

For each student
1	Activity Sheet 8

For each team of four
1	meterstick

For the class
1	*map, local
1 set	*models, planet (from Activity 6)
1 roll	paper, butcher
1 pair	*scissors
1 roll	tape, masking
1 roll	*tape, transparent

*provided by the teacher

Preparation

1. Make a copy of Activity Sheet 8 for each student.

2. Cut one 7.5-m (about 25-ft) strip from the roll of butcher paper. This strip of paper will become the backdrop for the classroom model of the Solar System as described in the activity. However, if your classroom walls (or school corridor walls) can accommodate a longer model, you may want to alter the scale.

3. On a local map, mark the location of your school. Then choose and mark a location or landmark that is 12 km (about 7.5 mi) from school as the crow flies. Next, choose and mark a place on the map that is 6 km (about 3.7 mi) from school. Finally, mark a spot on the map at 150 m (about 500 ft) from your classroom. You will need to refer to these locations in the discussion to determine a scale to use for the classroom model.

4. Each team of four will need a meterstick. The class will need one set of planet models from Activity 6.

Background Information

In a classroom model, the same scale cannot be used to represent both the relative sizes of planets and their relative distances from the Sun. At the same scale used to create the planet models (1 cm: 5,000 km), a scale model representing their relative distance from the Sun would position Pluto 12 km (about 7.5 miles) away from the model of the Sun! Therefore, the scale used to model the planets' distances from the Sun in this activity must be different from the scale used to calculate their sizes in Activity 6.

The greater the distances on the model of the Solar System, the stronger the model's visual impact, and the better students can appreciate the enormity of the actual distances between planets in space. Because most classrooms can accommodate a poster 7.5 m (about 25 ft) in length, the scale that students will use in this activity is based on that length.

In this activity, the scale students will use to measure the planets' relative distances from the Sun is 1 cm:9,000,000 km. You may need to choose a different one. The scale itself is not important. What is important is that distances be scaled so that students can visualize the relative distances of planets from the Sun.

Modeling Planet Distances

What do you know about the shape of a planet's orbit that makes it necessary to use the planet's average distance from the Sun as a measurement in the chart below? Use the terms *perihelion* and *aphelion* in your answer.

An orbit is not a circle, so average distance is used instead of a planet's distance when it is closest (at perihelion) or farthest (at aphelion) from the Sun.

Planet	Average Actual Distance from Sun (km)	Scale Model Distance from Sun (cm) Scale = 1 cm:9,000,000 km
Mercury	57,800,000	6.4
Venus	108,200,000	12.0
Earth	149,600,000	16.6
Mars	227,900,000	25.3
Jupiter	778,300,000	86.5
Saturn	1,429,400,000	158.8
Uranus	2,871,000,000	319.0
Neptune	4,501,200,000	500.0
Pluto	6,000,000,000	666.6

Refer to the chart above for the scaled distance from the Sun of each planet's orbit. On the model of the Solar System, measure out from the Sun the scaled distance for your assigned planet and make a dot on the paper. Position your planet model so that its center is over the dot. Tape your planet model in place on the paper.

Which two planets have their orbits between Earth and the Sun?

Mercury and Venus

Which two planets orbit at the greatest distance from the Sun?

Neptune and Pluto

Teaching Suggestions

Review the names of the nine planets in the order of their distance from the Sun.

Remind students that all planets are satellites, orbiting at different distances from the Sun. The greater their distances from the Sun, the larger their orbits.

Tell students that just as they scaled down the actual sizes of the planets in Activity 6 to model their relative sizes, they can scale down the actual distances between objects in the Solar System to make a model that shows the planets' relative distances from the Sun.

Explain that in this activity teams will make a scale model of the Solar System to help them visualize the relative distances of the planets from the Sun.

Review the orbits of the planets with students. Ask, **What shape are orbits? Is any planet always the same distance from the Sun?**

Ask, **What two terms describe the points along a planet's orbit at which the planet is closest to and farthest from the Sun?**

Tell students that since the distances at perihelion and aphelion are different, they cannot both be used to make the models. Only one distance measurement can be used. Write *average distance* on the board. Explain that to find the average distance of a planet from the Sun, the distances at perihelion and aphelion are added together and then divided by 2.

Tell students that both the actual average distance and the scaled-down average distance from the Sun of every planet's orbit have already been calculated and are shown on the activity sheet for them to use in making their scale models.

Additional Information

1 Encourage students to use their mnemonic devices from Activity 1 to name the planets in this order: Mercury, Venus, Earth, Mars, Jupiter, Saturn, Uranus, Neptune, and Pluto.

2 The shapes of orbits are elliptical (or ellipses). No, because orbits are elliptical, the distance of a planet from the Sun varies.

perihelion and aphelion, respectively

If necessary, demonstrate with a simple example on the board, such as adding 4 and 6 and dividing by 2 to get an average of 5.

Point out to students that although we talk about a planet's average distance from the Sun, we are actually referring to the average distance of the planetary orbit from the Sun.

Planet	Average Actual Distance from Sun (km)	Scale Model Distance from Sun (cm) Scale = 1 cm:9,000,000 km
Mercury	57,800,000	6.4
Venus	108,200,000	12.0
Earth	149,600,000	16.6
Mars	227,900,000	25.3
Jupiter	778,300,000	86.5
Saturn	1,429,400,000	158.8
Uranus	2,871,000,000	319.0
Neptune	4,501,200,000	500.0
Pluto	6,000,000,000	666.6

Figure 8-1. Actual and scale model planetary distances from the Sun.

Refer to Figure 8-1. On the board, write *Earth* and *Pluto* and their average actual distances from the Sun, as shown in the chart. Say the number of millions of kilometers aloud and emphasize to students that these distances are enormous.

Most students will have a hard time comprehending distances this great.

Emphasize that students must scale down those distances in order to visualize the relative distances of the planets from one another and from the Sun.

Explain that by constructing a scale model that will fit inside the classroom, they can get a better idea of the relative distances between planets in the Solar System.

Ask, **Do you think you could use the same scale for your Solar System model that you used for your planets?**

Answers will vary.

Explain to students that if they used the same scale—1 cm:5,000 km—they would have to put the model of Pluto 12 km (about 7.5 miles) away from the model of the Sun!

To illustrate that distance, show students the local map you prepared earlier showing their school and the point you marked 12 km away.

If students are familiar with the area around the school, name the location or landmark you show them on the map.

Lead students to conclude that they cannot use this scale for their Solar System model.

4

Write the ratio *1 m:1,000,000 km* on the board. Ask, **How far would a model of Earth be from a model of the Sun if you were to scale its distance to this ratio?**

149.6 m

Help students scale the distance by writing the scale and doing the calculation on the board. At the scale of 1 m:1,000,000 km, 149,600,000 km becomes 149.6 m, approximately the length of one and one-half football fields.

Again, show students the local map you prepared and point out the spot where the Earth model would be—150 m from school.

Ask, **How far would a model of Pluto be from a model of the Sun at this scale?**

6,000 m

Help students scale the distance. Do the calculation on the board. At the scale of 1 m:1,000,000 km, 6,000,000,000 km becomes 6,000 m, or 6 km, which is approximately 3.7 miles.

Show students the local map again and point out the place you marked that is 6 km from school.

5

Review the results of using the 1 m: 1,000,000 km scale: remind students that at this scale, if the classroom were the Sun, Earth would be about 150 m away, and Pluto would be 6 km away.

Ask, **Is this the scale to use if our Solar System model is to fit inside the classroom?**

Every student's response should be no.

Tell students that instead they will use a scale that will allow their model to fit in the classroom. The scale is 1 cm:9,000,000 km.

Explain that they will use a strip of paper 7.5 m (about 25 ft) long as a backdrop for

their model of the Solar System. Remind
teams that they made a set of planet models
in Activity 6.

Distribute a copy of Activity Sheet 8 to each
student. Call students' attention to the
chart on the activity sheet giving the
(average) actual and scaled distances from
the Sun of each planet. Point out that the
actual distances are given in kilometers and
the scaled distances for their model are
given in centimeters.

Refer to Figure 8-2 and draw a long
rectangle on the board that represents the
paper backdrop for their model. Draw the
arc that represents the edge of a model Sun,
as shown in the figure. Explain that a model
of the Sun made to the same scale as their
planet models would be 2.8 m (about 9.3 ft)
in diameter.

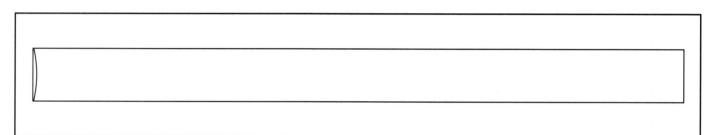

Figure 8-2. The arc of a model Sun.

Tell students that a model of the entire Sun,
even if reduced to this scale, is too large to
fit on the paper. They will draw only a
shallow curve to represent the edge of the
Sun on the left-hand side of the strip of
paper.

Explain that they will measure the scaled
distance for each planet model from the
curved edge of the Sun out along the length
of the strip of paper. They will make a dot
with a pencil and then tape each planet
model to the paper so that the center of
each model is over the dot.

Remind students that they are to use the scale-
model distance in centimeters shown on their activity
sheet to measure from the Sun's arc to each model
planet.

Assign each team a specific planet model (or
models, depending on the number of teams
working together) to display on the
backdrop.

If fewer than eight teams will be working on the
project, apportion the nine planets among the teams
so that the team with the fewest planets to mount is
responsible for putting up the backdrop on the
classroom wall and drawing the arc of the Sun.

Distribute a meterstick to each team. Give the 7.5-m rolled strip of butcher paper and the roll of masking tape to the team assigned to mount the backdrop on the wall. Have the transparent tape available for teams to share. Distribute to teams their assigned planet model(s).

Have teams begin making the model of the Solar System.

Remind students that the planets are in constant orbit around the Sun and are not lined up in a row as indicated in the simplified classroom model.

After teams have finished modeling the scaled distances of the planets on the strip of paper, begin a discussion of their scale model.

Ask, **Which planet is farther from the Sun, Earth or Mercury? Which orbit around the Sun is larger, Mercury's orbit or Earth's orbit?**

Earth; Earth's orbit

Ask, **Which planet is closer to the Sun, Jupiter or Pluto? Which orbit around the Sun is smaller, Jupiter's orbit or Pluto's orbit?**

Jupiter; Jupiter's orbit

Reinforcement

Have students discuss the relative distances between several pairs of planets. For example, ask, **Is the distance from Saturn to Jupiter greater or less than the distance from Earth to Mars?**

Cleanup

Have students return the metersticks and roll of masking tape to the kit. Any unused butcher paper should be replaced in the kit. The class model of the Solar System should remain displayed for students to examine and discuss at least until after the last activity in the module is conducted.

Connections

Science Challenge

Tell students that if they wanted to use real objects to accurately show the planets' relative sizes and distances from the Sun, they would have to set up a huge model, such as the one described below. (Also see Science and Social Studies below.)

	Model Size	Distance from Model Sun
Sun	4-ft balloon	—
Mercury	head of nail	100 yards
Venus	marble	200 yards
Earth	marble	250 yards
Mars	pea	350 yards
Jupiter	cantaloupe	0.5 mile
Saturn	softball	1 mile
Uranus	billiard ball	2 miles
Neptune	billiard ball	3 miles
Pluto	head of pin	3.5 miles

Science Extension

Ask the "Uranus" team to report additional information they have found and to record Uranus's data on the class master chart.

Additional Facts About Uranus
Volume (Earth = 1): 67
Mass (Earth = 1): 14.5
Density (water = 1): 1.29
Temperature at cloud tops: –346°F (–210°C)
Composition: rocky core, layer of water, ammonia, and methane
Names of major moons: Umbriel, Ariel, Titania, Oberon, Miranda
Distinctive features: axis of rotation is tilted at almost 98° from plane of orbit

The following activity shows that an object's distance from a heat source affects the object's temperature. Instruct teams as follows: Put one thermometer 10 cm and another thermometer 100 cm from the base of a desk lamp, and record the two temperatures. Turn the lamp on, and record both temperatures at 10-minute intervals for an hour. The closer thermometer will show higher temperatures. (Also see Science and Math below.)

Science and Language Arts

Tell students to imagine they are passengers on a spaceship traveling through the Solar System. Ask them to write short stories describing the voyage and their observations as they approach, orbit, and then leave each planet. Let students share their stories.

Science and Math

Help students construct a bar graph or line graph of the data they recorded in the second Science Extension above. Tell them to label the vertical axis *Temperature* and the horizontal axis *Time*, with the 10-minute intervals noted, and to plot each thermometer's data in a different color.

Science and Social Studies

The March 1995 issue of *Discover* magazine contains a delightful article, "The Planets of Peoria" by Jeffrey Klugar, describing the world's largest model of the Solar System. Built to a scale of 42 feet:1 million miles, the model uses the 36-foot-wide dome of a planetarium to represent the Sun and positions the planets at their correct relative sizes and distances. Mercury, for example, is 1.5 inches in diameter and located a quarter-mile away—in a school supply store; 3.8-inch Venus is in an insurance agency office a half-mile from Mercury. If your students can appreciate the tongue-in-cheek tone of the article and can understand its adult language level, read it aloud to the class or provide copies for them to read on their own. Interested students might like to create a similar model in their town.

Activity 9
Days and Years

Objectives

In this activity, students investigate which two motions of a planet determine the length of its days and years. They also discover the relationship between the length of a planet's year and its distance from the Sun.

The students
- distinguish between rotation and revolution
- construct and operate a model to demonstrate planetary rotation
- role-play planets revolving around the Sun

Schedule

Session I – About 40 minutes
Session II – About 50 minutes

Vocabulary

axis
day
revolution
rotation
year

Materials

For each student
1   Activity Sheet 9

For each team of four
1   *model, satellite (from Activity 2)
1 pair   *scissors

For the class
2   bulbs, 100-watt
1 set   *labels, Names of Planets (from Activity 1)
2   light sources
8   metersticks
1   *model, satellite (from Activity 2)
1 pair   *scissors
1 ball   string
1 roll   tape, masking

*provided by the teacher

Preparation

Session I
1. Make a copy of Activity Sheet 9 for each student.

2. Disassemble the demonstration satellite model from Activity 2. Insert the plastic tube into the foam ball so that its ends protrude equally on both sides of the ball (see Figure 9-1).

3. Each team of four will need a satellite model from Activity 2 and a pair of scissors. Teams will share the light sources.

4. Have extension cords handy in case they are needed for the light sources.

Session II
1. Plan to conduct Session II at a time when the class can visit a large open area of the school yard.

2. Assign roles of Sun and planets to 10 students, or ask for volunteers. (Or you might have them draw lots for the roles.) Have the other students help measure and mark distances in the

school yard and help manage the lengths of string.

3. Make ten copies of Figure 9-3, one for yourself and nine for the students who will use the metersticks to measure distances outside.

4. If students role-play planets orbiting the Sun at the distances given in Figure 9-3 (at the scale of 1 m:9,000,000 km), it may be feasible to have only the closest four or five "planets" of the nine actually "revolve" around the student "Sun." Then, if space permits, you might have the others measure or pace off their distances and then stand still rather than walk their circles.

5. When they go outside, students will need to take the string, scissors, metersticks, and copies of Figure 9-3.

Background Information

The *axis* of a planet is an imaginary line, or axle, through the center of that planet. The points where the ends of the imaginary axle protrude from a planet are called the *poles*.

Each planet spins about its axis. One complete turn of a planet is called a *rotation*. The time it takes for any planet to make one complete rotation is called a *day*. Each planet rotates at a different speed, so the lengths of their days are different. A day on Jupiter is less than 10 hours, but a day on Mercury is 1406 hours long.

One complete orbit of a planet around the Sun is called a *revolution*. The time it takes for a planet to complete one revolution is called a *year*. Planets travel at different speeds and different distances in their orbits. Therefore, the length of a year on each planet is different. The farther a planet is from the Sun, the longer its year. A year on Mercury is equal to about 88 Earth days, but it takes Pluto about 248 Earth years to make one revolution around the Sun.

So even though on any given planet 1 day is equal to one rotation, and 1 year is equal to one revolution, each planet has a unique day length and year length.

Name _____   Activity Sheet 9

Days and Years

1. Complete these sentences:

   A day is the time it takes a planet to complete one ___rotation___ about its axis.

   A year is the time it takes a planet to complete one *revolution* around the Sun.

2. Disassemble the satellite model. Put the plastic tube into the hole in the foam ball so that the ends of the tube stick out on both sides of the ball. This is your Earth model. Use one end of the tube as a handle and spin the ball as you would you spin a top.

   As you spin the model, are you simulating days or years? *days*

3. Go to one of the light sources. Hold the Earth model by the tube and near the light. Rotate the ball once.

   What do you notice about how much of the model is lit and how much is dark?

   Half of the ball is lit and half is dark.

   Do the sizes of the light and dark areas change when you rotate the Earth model? *No.*

   What do the light and dark areas represent on Earth?

   day and night

4. Continue to hold the model by the tube, but now move the ball around the light source. What are you simulating now, a day or a year? *a year*

5. Make one revolution with your model close to the light source. Now, move the model farther away from the light source and make another revolution, moving the model at the same speed.

   Which revolution took longer? *the one with the model farther from the light source*

   If planets have orbits of different sizes, will all planets make one revolution in the same length of time? *No.*

   Does a planet with a very large orbit take more time to make one revolution around the Sun? If so, which planet has the longest year? *Yes: Pluto.*

Teaching Suggestions

Additional Information

1

Show students the demonstration Earth model—the foam ball with the tube through its center.

Write *axis* on the board. Explain that the axis describes an imaginary line through the center of a planet. Ask them to imagine the foam ball is a planet and the plastic tube is its axis.

Explain that, in addition to orbiting the Sun, planets also spin about their axes. Write the words *rotate* and *rotation* on the board. Tell students rotate means to spin, or turn around, and that a rotation is one complete turn of a planet as it spins about its imaginary axis.

Demonstrate the rotation of a planet by turning the tube to make the foam ball turn around once.

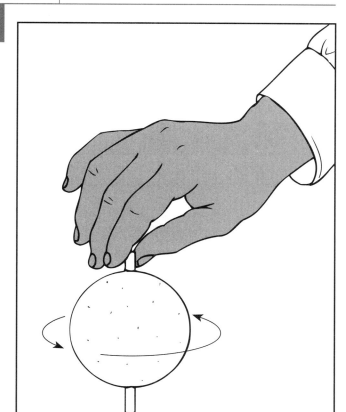

Figure 9-1. An Earth model.

Write the word *day* on the board and ask, **How would you define a day?**

Many students will respond that a day is 24 hours long.

Explain that a day is the time it takes for any planet to make one complete rotation about its axis. On planet Earth we divide our day into 24 hours. It takes 24 hours for Earth to make one rotation about its axis.

Again, turn the model around once to simulate Earth's rotation.

Write the word *year* on the board and ask, **How would you define a year?**

2

Students may know a year is 365 days, but they may not be able to define a year in terms of a planet's orbit around the Sun.

Explain that a year is the time it takes a planet to travel once around the Sun. Earth rotates about 365 times as it makes one orbit around the Sun. An Earth year, then, is about 365 days long.

Planet Name	Day Length	Year Length
Mercury	58.6 Earth days	88 Earth days
Venus	243 Earth days	226.5 Earth days
Earth	23 hours 56 minutes	365.25 Earth days
Mars	24 hours 37 minutes	687 Earth days
Jupiter	9 hours 55 minutes	11.9 Earth years
Saturn	10 hours 40 minutes	29.5 Earth years
Uranus	17 hours 14 minutes	84 Earth years
Neptune	18 hours	164.8 Earth years
Pluto	6 Earth days 10 hours	248 Earth years

Figure 9-2. The lengths of days and years on the planets.

Write the words *revolve* and *revolution* on the board. Tell students that planets revolve, or travel around, the Sun in their orbits. A revolution is one complete trip of a planet around the Sun.

3 Again hold up the demonstration ball and tube. Tell students that in this activity they will modify their satellite models from Activity 2 to construct a planet model like the one you are holding.

Tell them they will cut the fishing line and remove it from the foam ball and the plastic tube, putting aside the washer tied to the line. Then they will push the tube through the hole in the foam ball, as shown in the demonstration model.

Tell students that in this activity they will use one end of the tube as a handle to rotate and revolve the foam balls to simulate a day and a year.

4 Distribute a copy of Activity Sheet 9 to each student. Give each team a satellite model from Activity 2 and a pair of scissors. Ask them to complete Steps 1 and 2 and then give you their attention.

As soon as teams have finished simulating days by spinning their models like tops, ask, **What do the tube and the ball in the model represent?**

Earth's axis and Earth

Explain that all the planets in our Solar System rotate, but they all rotate at different speeds. One rotation of any planet is called a day, no matter how long it takes to make that rotation.

Set up the light sources at opposite ends of the room. Have each team gather around one of the two light sources.

Ask, **What do you think the light bulb will represent in this activity?**

Lead students to conclude that it will represent the Sun.

Remind students that from our viewpoint here on Earth, we see the Sun rise in the morning, move across the sky, and set in the evening. It appears to be moving around Earth. Ask, **Recalling what you know about the Solar System, does the Sun move around Earth?**

All students should answer no—Earth moves around the Sun.

Explain that it is Earth's rotation about its axis that makes the Sun appear to move around Earth.

Have students complete their activity sheets, beginning with Step 3.

When all students have finished, have them recall their simulation of a year. Ask, **Which revolution took a longer period of time, the one with the model held close to the light or the one with the model held farther away from the light?**

The farther away the model was from the light, the longer the time it took to complete one revolution.

Ask, **Based on your observations, which planet would you say has the longest year?**

Pluto

Tell students that in the next session, they will go outside and take part in a demonstration showing the relationship between length of a year and the distance traveled during an orbit.

Have students disassemble the models. Have them return the foam balls, plastic tubes, washers, and light sources with bulbs to the kit.

Explain to students that in this part of the activity they will model the Solar System outdoors on a larger scale than they did their classroom model in Activity 8. Ten students will role-play the Sun and planets on a scale of 1 meter to 90 million kilometers instead of 1 centimeter to 9 million kilometers.

Before they go outside, have the students who will play the Sun and planets identify themselves with the labels from Activity 1, attaching the labels to the front of their clothing with masking tape.

Take students outside and into an open area of the school yard. Take along nine copies of Figure 9-3, eight metersticks, the balls of string, and scissors.

Choose a central point in the largest open area of the school yard and have the student "Sun" stand still at that point. Beginning with the scaled distance to the closest planet, have students use metersticks and scissors to measure and cut lengths of string to the longest scaled distances on Figure 9-3 the school yard will accommodate. (Keep in mind that these distances are radii of the planets' orbits; double them to estimate the diameters of the circles students will walk.)

Remind students that although orbits are elliptical, for the sake of this demonstration they will walk in circular orbits showing the planets' average distances from the Sun.

Planet Name	Average Distance from Sun (km)	Model distance from "Sun" (m) Scale = 1 m:90,000,000 km
Mercury	57,800,000	0.6
Venus	108,200,000	1.2
Earth	149,600,000	1.7
Mars	227,900,000	2.5
Jupiter	778,300,000	8.7
Saturn	1,429,400,000	15.9
Uranus	2,871,000,000	31.9
Neptune	4,501,200,000	50.0
Pluto	6,000,000,000	66.6

Figure 9-3. School yard-scaled distances.

Tie one end of all the strings together for the "Sun" to hold over his or her head so they will not tangle as students walk their "orbits." Give the other end of each string to a student "planet" to hold, beginning with "Mercury." Align students so that they stand in a straight line out from the "Sun," as on their Solar System models.

If school yard area is limited, have the outermost student "planets" measure or pace their scaled distances from the "Sun" and stand still at that distance.

At the scale provided (1 m:90,000,000 km), Pluto would be 66.6 m (about 218 ft) away from the Sun. Pluto's scaled orbit would be a circle 133 m (about 437 ft) in diameter (about 1.5 times the length of a football field).

Have the "planets" walk at equal paces around the "Sun," staying in their orbits.

After everyone is back in the classroom, begin a discussion of their observations during the outdoor activity.

Ask, **Why is the length of a year on a planet far away from the Sun longer than the length of a year on a planet closer to the Sun?**

Encourage answers using the terms *revolve* and *revolution.* A planet far away has a much greater distance to travel in one revolution around the Sun than does a planet closer to the Sun.

Explain that each planet travels in its orbit at a different speed. Some planets travel faster than others. Even though some planets revolve faster than others, the outer planets take longer to complete their orbits because of their greater distances from the Sun.

Remind students that one revolution of any planet is called a year, no matter how long in Earth time it takes to make that revolution.

Reinforcement

Have students use the data for day length and year length in Figure 9-2 to make a separate card for each planet, with its day length noted in one color and its year length noted in another color. First have students arrange the cards in order from the shortest to the longest year length. Then have them arrange them in order of the shortest to the longest day length. Have them use the terms *rotation, day, revolution,* and *year* to explain why the order is different in the two arrangements.

Cleanup

Have students remove and discard the pieces of masking tape from the planet labels and return the labels to the kit along with the roll of masking tape, metersticks, and ball of string. The cut lengths of string may be either discarded or rewound and saved for later use.

Connections

Science Challenge

Demonstrate the cause of the changing seasons using a globe to represent Earth and a desk lamp to represent the Sun. Start with Earth's axis tilted toward the Sun, and explain that this shows Earth's position in June, the beginning of summer in the Northern Hemisphere where we live. Move Earth to its autumn, winter, and spring positions in its orbit, making sure you keep the axis tilted in the same direction (not toward the Sun) throughout the entire orbit. At each seasonal position, ask students to note the angle at which the Sun's light rays strike the Northern Hemisphere. If students have difficulty relating the tilt of the axis to seasonal changes, repeat the demonstration with the axis held straight up and down through the orbit. Students will see that without the tilt, any place on Earth receives the Sun's rays at the same angle in all seasons.

Science Extension

Ask the "Neptune" team to report additional information they have found and to record Neptune's data on the class master chart.

Additional Facts About Neptune
Volume (Earth = 1): 57
Mass (Earth = 1): 17.14
Density (water = 1): 1.64
Temperature at cloud tops: –345°F (–210°C)
Composition: small rocky core, layer of
    water, ammonia, and methane
Names of major moons: Triton, Nereid,
    Proteus, Despina, Thalassa, Naiad
Distinctive features: sea-blue atmosphere
    has two storm systems—the Great Dark
    Spot and Dark Spot 2—and one white
    cloud called *Scooter* because of its rapid
    movement; highly changeable weather
    discovered with Hubble telescope

Science and Math

Have students use the year lengths given in Figure 9-2 to calculate their ages on other planets. (Tell students to round off their ages to the nearest year.) For example, a student who is 12 years old would be almost 50 years old on Mercury, slightly more than 1 year old on Jupiter, and 0.14 year old on Uranus. Help students decide on the appropriate math operations for each planet. (For planets with year lengths shorter than Earth's, multiply Earth age by 365 days, then divide by the planet's year length. For planets with longer year lengths, divide Earth age by the planet's year length.)

Tell students that Earth's circumference—the distance around Earth measured at the equator—is about 40,000 km (24,900 mi.). Then ask: If you stood on the equator, how fast would you be traveling in kilometers per hour? (circumference ÷ 24 hours = 1,667 kph, 1,037 mph)

Science, Technology, and Society

Give teams the following instructions for making a simple sundial: Secure a pencil upright in an empty thread spool glued to the center of a sheet of stiff, light-colored poster board. Put this sundial base in a location where it will get sun throughout the entire day. Use a compass to align the base north-south, and mark S on its south-facing edge. At the next full hour on a clock, mark the pencil's shadow on the poster board and label the line with the hour. Continue doing this every hour throughout the day. Once all possible hours are marked, students can use the sundial to tell time in any sunlit location so long as it is correctly aligned north-south.

Activity 10
Asteroids, Meteoroids, and Comets

Objectives

Students investigate other satellites of the Sun in our Solar System besides planets— asteroids, meteoroids, and comets.

The students
- investigate asteroids, meteoroids, and comets
- examine a frozen model of a comet head
- draw a comet at various points on its elliptical orbit

Schedule

Session I – About 40 minutes
Session II – About 30 minutes

Vocabulary

asteroid
asteroid belt
comet
crater
friction
meteor
meteorite
meteoroid

Materials

For each student
1   Activity Sheet 10

For each team of four
1   *crayon, red
1   pan, aluminum

For the class
8   cups, paper, soufflé
8   cups, plastic
1   *marker, black
1   *match, safety
1   *model, Solar System (from Activity 8)
1   pan, aluminum
1 sht   *paper, plain
30–35   *pebbles
1 pair   *rubber gloves (optional)
1 pair   *safety goggles
1 pad   steel wool
1 pair   tweezers
          *water, muddy

*provided by the teacher

Preparation

Session I
Pull a 2.5-cm (about 1-in.) piece of steel wool from the pad. (It is a good idea to wear rubber gloves to protect your fingers from splinters when you handle steel wool.) Spread the piece out until it is roughly spherical and about 5 cm (about 2 in.) in diameter with many air spaces. Place it in an aluminum pan and have the safety goggles, safety match, and pair of tweezers ready for use in the activity (see Figure 10-1).

Session II
1. Prepare eight comet head models the day before the activity. To make each comet head, place a few pebbles and some muddy water in a soufflé cup and freeze the mixture. Transfer the frozen contents of each soufflé cup to the larger plastic cup, nearly fill the plastic cup with water, and return it to the freezer. Be sure to keep the comet heads frozen until Step 12.

2. Make a copy of Activity Sheet 10 for each student.

3. Each team of four will need a red crayon, a comet head model, and an aluminum pan.

Background Information

Other kinds of satellites orbit the Sun in our Solar System besides the nine principal planets and their moons. Much smaller bits of matter also revolve around the Sun.

Asteroids are tiny planets, and although most are no larger than 1.5 km (about 1 mi) in diameter, the largest has a diameter of more than 1,000 km (about 600 mi). Of the estimated millions of asteroids in the Solar System, most are concentrated in an area between the orbits of Mars and Jupiter called the *asteroid belt.*

Meteoroids are small bits of matter—debris from comets and fragments of rock and metal like miniature asteroids—that also orbit the Sun. If a meteoroid's orbit brings it too close to a planet, the planet's gravity captures the meteoroid and pulls it faster and faster toward the planet's surface. If the planet has an atmosphere, friction is generated by the meteoroid's rubbing against the particles of the atmosphere. As the speed of the meteoroid increases, so does the friction.

As the friction increases, the meteoroid heats up and begins to burn and glow. Now it is called a *meteor* (also known as a shooting star). Any part of the meteor that does not burn up completely in the atmosphere and eventually hits the planet's surface is called a *meteorite.* The indentation it makes as it crashes into the planet's surface is called a *crater.*

Comets can be compared to huge, dirty snowballs of ice-covered dust and rock particles, each a mile or more across. Their elliptical orbits around the Sun are far longer than planetary orbits, carrying them far from the Sun at aphelion (see Figure 10-2). As a comet approaches perihelion, the Sun's radiation begins to vaporize its icy covering, sending gases and fine particles streaming away from the comet's head in a shining "tail." It is the sunlight reflecting off particles in the comet's tail that makes the comet visible to us on Earth.

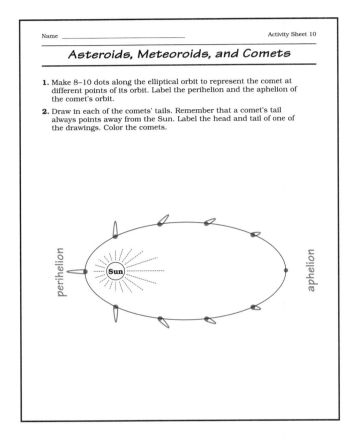

Name _____   Activity Sheet 10

Asteroids, Meteoroids, and Comets

1. Make 8–10 dots along the elliptical orbit to represent the comet at different points of its orbit. Label the perihelion and the aphelion of the comet's orbit.

2. Draw in each of the comets' tails. Remember that a comet's tail always points away from the Sun. Label the head and tail of one of the drawings. Color the comets.

Teaching Suggestions

Additional Information

Begin the discussion by asking, **What objects are satellites of the Sun?**	**1** planets
Do you think the Sun has any other satellites?	Allow students to speculate.
Explain that there are other types of objects orbiting the Sun and that they will investigate them in this activity.	

2 Write the word *asteroid* on the board. Explain that an asteroid is a very small, rocky planet that orbits the Sun.

Tell students that astronomers estimate that there are millions of asteroids in our Solar System. Most are no larger than 1.5 km (about 1 mi) across, but the largest is more than 1,000 km (about 600 mi) in diameter.

Ask for a volunteer to stand near the Sun in front of the classroom model of the Solar System and point out the area between the orbits of Mars and Jupiter.

Write *asteroid belt* on the board. Tell students that most of the asteroids are orbiting in a wide band of space between Mars and Jupiter known as the asteroid belt.

Ask for another volunteer to take a black marker and go to the Solar System model. Have the student draw 20 or 30 scattered dots of different sizes on the model to represent asteroids orbiting in the asteroid belt.

Ask for a third volunteer to use the marker to label this area *The Asteroid Belt*.

3 Call students' attention to the board and write the words *meteoroid, meteor, meteorite,* and *crater* on the board. Ask, **What do you think these are?**

Again, allow students to speculate.

Explain that meteoroids are like miniature asteroids, chunks of rock and metal that orbit the Sun.

Meteors and meteorites will be discussed later.

Ask, **What is the name of the force that might attract a meteoroid toward a planet?**

gravity

Remind students that gravity is a force that pulls objects together.

Ask, **What would happen if a meteoroid's orbit brought it close to a planet?**

Most students will say that the meteoroid could be pulled toward the planet.

Explain that if an asteroid or meteoroid is pulled toward a planet by the force of gravity, the asteroid or meteoroid might behave in one of several ways: it might come near but continue to travel past the planet; it might go into orbit around the planet; or it might be pulled all the way to a planet's surface.

Ask, **What would happen if the asteroid or meteoroid were pulled all the way to the surface of the planet?**

4 Students may know about craters caused by meteoroids crashing to the surface of Earth or the Moon.

Tell students that when a meteoroid enters a planet's atmosphere, it begins to burn and glow white-hot as it is pulled toward the planet's surface. As it burns up it is called a *meteor.*

Ask, **Who has ever seen a shooting star?**

Ask for a show of hands of students who have seen a shooting star.

Explain that a shooting star is actually a meteor burning in the Earth's atmosphere.

Explain that a meteor does not always burn up completely in the atmosphere. Sometimes a chunk of rock or metal survives the journey to the surface. The piece that crashes into the planet is called a *meteorite.* The impact may form a crater, a bowl-shaped depression in the planet's surface.

Remind students that a meteor is a meteoroid that is in the process of burning up in the atmosphere. Ask, **What do you think causes the meteor to burn?**

 5

Accept all speculations.

Have each student hold a pencil near one end and ask, **What is the temperature of the pencil relative to the temperature of the air?**

The temperatures are nearly the same.

Now have each student hold the pencil near one end with one hand while they rub the shaft of the pencil rapidly back and forth with the thumb and forefinger of the other hand.

Ask, **What is happening to the temperature of your finger, thumb, and pencil?**

They are getting warmer.

 Write the word *friction* on the board. Explain that friction is the rubbing together of two surfaces.

Tell students that the friction of the finger and thumb rubbing rapidly against the pencil caused the heat they felt.

Ask, **Do you think an object moving through the atmosphere encounters friction?**

Responses will vary.

Hold a sheet of paper horizontally and let it fall to the floor. Ask, **Knowing what you do about the pulling force of gravity, why did the paper not fall straight down to the floor?**

Some students may say the air under the paper kept it from falling straight down.

Explain that as the paper fell, it pushed against the molecules of air—the particles of Earth's atmosphere. Although the particles are invisible, we can see their effect—they prevented the paper from falling straight down to the floor.

Explain that as a fast-moving object, such as a meteoroid, pushes through the particles of a planet's atmosphere, it encounters friction.

 Ask, **What will happen to the meteoroid as it continues to push its way through the atmosphere toward a planet's surface?**

Encourage responses that include the terms *friction* and *meteor.*

Remind students that a meteor, or shooting star, looks bright because it is burning as a result of friction with the atmosphere.

Ask, **What is the meteor called if it hits Earth before it burns up completely?**

a meteorite

Tell students that many of the meteorites found on Earth are made mostly of metal. Ask, **Can metal burn? Can it glow?**

Responses may vary.

Tell students that you will demonstrate to the class what it might be like for a meteoroid to become so hot that it glows and becomes a meteor.

Obtain the aluminum pan, steel wool, tweezers, safety goggles, and the safety match. Show students an unburned piece of steel wool. Explain that steel wool is loosely woven strands of steel, a metal.

 Put on the safety goggles.

Hold the piece of steel wool with the tweezers over the aluminum pan. Light the match and bring the flame of the match into contact with the steel wool. Ask, **What is happening?**

The steel wool is beginning to glow and burn.

Explain that just as the steel wool burns and gives off light, so does a meteor in the atmosphere.

Discuss again the sequence of events that cause a meteoroid to become first a meteor and then a meteorite.

9

Figure 10-1. Simulating a meteor.

Ask, **What force pulls a meteoroid toward Earth?**

gravity

Ask, **What causes the meteor to heat up and burn?**

friction between the meteor and Earth's atmosphere

Review with students the series of events. A meteoroid encounters friction as it is pulled by gravity through the atmosphere. As it glows and burns in the atmosphere, it becomes a meteor. If the meteor does not completely burn up in the atmosphere, whatever is left crashes into the surface of the planet and is then called a *meteorite*.

Tell students that in Session II they will investigate comets, still another type of satellite.

Session II

Begin by asking, **What do you think a comet is?**

Many students will respond that comets are bright objects that fly through our Solar System.

Explain that a comet is a small rocky mass, usually less than 2 km (about 1.25 mi) in diameter, trapped in ice—frozen water and other kinds of ice that would be gases on Earth. Just as planets do, comets orbit the Sun in elliptical orbits, but their orbits stretch farther, sometimes taking them out away from the Sun to several hundred times the distance of Pluto. Viewed from Earth, comets look like bright glowing spots with long tails streaming behind as they travel through space.

Ask, **What do you think makes a comet visible to us on Earth?**

11

Responses will be varied.

Tell students that there is no atmosphere in space. Therefore, a comet does not encounter enough friction in space to cause it to heat up and burn. Tell students that it is so cold in outer space that the ice around the surface of a comet does not melt. But when a comet's orbit brings it close to the Sun, some of the ice begins to evaporate.

Ask, **What is the point in an orbit called where a satellite is closest to the Sun?**

perihelion

Point out that when the ice turns to vapor, particles of dust trapped in the ice break free. Radiation streaming out from the Sun pushes this material away from the comet in a long tail that always points away from the Sun. These particles reflect sunlight, and it is this reflected sunlight that makes the comet visible to us on Earth.

Students may be familiar with Halley's Comet.

Tell students that they will investigate models of comets.

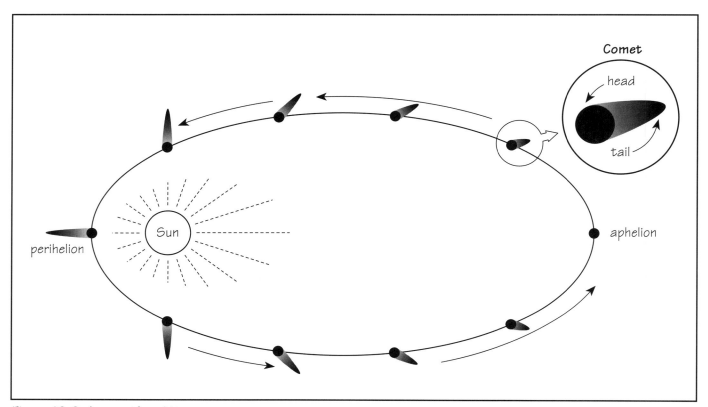

Figure 10-2. A comet's orbit.

Give each student a copy of Activity Sheet 10. Distribute a model comet head in an aluminum pan and a red crayon to each team.

Encourage students to examine the model comet head from time to time for the rest of the activity period and observe any changes in it.

Tell students to complete Activity Sheet 10. Remind them to label the perihelion and aphelion of the orbit and the head and tail of the comet. Also remind them that a comet is shaped like a ball until it begins to approach the Sun. Then it begins to develop a tail, which always points away from the Sun, and is longest when it is closest to the Sun. Tell them to show these changes in their drawings.

After teams have completed their activity sheets, ask, **What do you think would happen if a comet orbiting the Sun passed close to a planet?**

Some students may suggest that the comet would collide with the planet.

Explain that sometimes, as a comet orbits the Sun, it encounters the gravitational pull of a large planet. The comet may then begin to orbit the planet that captured it.

Ask, **Is there a difference between what makes a comet visible and what makes a meteor visible?**

Encourage responses that distinguish between the reflected sunlight of a comet and the emitted light from a burning meteor.

Remind students that a comet is visible because sunlight reflects off a tail made of vapor and dust particles, whereas a meteor is visible because the friction it encounters in the atmosphere causes it to burn brightly.

Reinforcement

Ask students to think of three examples of objects that shine or glow from reflected light and three examples of objects that shine or glow because they are creating

their own light. (reflected light from water, a mirror, polished metal, and so on; burning light from a match, light bulb, candle, and so on)

Cleanup

Have students discard the liquid from the comet heads. If appropriate, have them save the pebbles. Tell them to rinse, air-dry, and

C return the aluminum pans to the kit. Plastic cups, remaining steel wool, and tweezers should be replaced in the kit.

Science at Home

Have students shine a flashlight in a darkened room through the dusty cloud made by slapping a cushioned piece of

furniture to demonstrate why a comet's tail shines.

Connections

Science Challenge

Tell students that astronomers searched for a ninth planet for many years before finally discovering Pluto in 1930. However, recent discoveries have led many astronomers to conclude that Pluto is not a major planet but only one of many small bodies called *planetesimals* that orbit the Sun beyond Neptune. Interested students may want to investigate this issue further.

Science Extension

Ask the "Pluto" team to report additional information they have found and to record Pluto's data on the class master chart.

Additional Facts About Pluto
Mass (Earth = 1): 0.0022
Density (water = 1): 2.03
Surface temperature: –364°F (–220°C)
Composition: large rocky core, layer of water ice, layer of water and methane ice
Name of moon: Charon
Distinctive features: odd orbit overlaps Neptune's orbit, bringing Pluto closer than Neptune to the Sun twice in each revolution

Explain that some meteors occur in groups, called meteor "showers," at specific times of the year. Obtain a list of the major meteor showers (one good source is *Sky Dragons and Flaming Swords* by Marietta D. Moskin; Walker, 1985) and make a copy for each student. Encourage students to look for these meteor showers when they are next scheduled to occur.

Science and Language Arts

Ask students to imagine that they are a meteoroid traveling through space. Have each student write a poem or short story about his or her experiences as a meteoroid, then a meteor in Earth's atmosphere, and finally a meteorite crashing to Earth's surface.

The classic children's book *The Little Prince* by Antoine de Saint Exupery is a charming allegorical tale of a man who meets a visitor from space—a little boy whose tiny home is "Asteroid B-612." If the book's comprehension level and allegorical content are appropriate for your class, provide a copy for students to read on their own, or read it aloud to them in several sessions. Give students an opportunity to discuss their responses to the story. Also discuss the differences between the fantasy asteroid and actual asteroids.

Science and Math

Tell students that Halley's comet travels in a huge elliptical orbit around the Sun, passing by Earth every 75–76 years. It last appeared in 1986. Ask students to calculate the year of the comet's next visit (2061–2062) and how old they will be at that time.

Science and Social Studies

If any students have visited Meteor Crater in Arizona, ask them to describe what they saw. Encourage interested students to find out the locations of other known meteorite impact sites in the United States and worldwide. Help students plot these locations on a globe or world map.

Science, Technology, and Society

Tell students that in July 1995, two United States amateur astronomers discovered a new and unusually bright comet far from the Sun. Named Hale-Bopp after its discoverers, the comet will come closest to the Sun in 1997, when it may become visible from Earth with the naked eye. Suggest that students watch for further news about Hale-Bopp in newspaper and television reports.

Activity 11
Star Light, Star Bright

Objectives

In this activity students explore the space beyond the Sun and its planets. They study other stars and discover that enormous distances separate them from one another and from our Solar System.

The students

■ use the term *light-year* in discussing distances from Earth to distant stars

■ investigate the relative brightness of light sources at various distances

■ are introduced to the concepts of *galaxy* and *universe*

Schedule

About 40 minutes

Vocabulary

Alpha Centauri
galaxy
light-year
Milky Way
North Star
relative brightness
universe

Materials

For each student
1   Activity Sheet 11

For each team of four
2   batteries, AA-size

2   batteries, D-size
1   flashlight
1   penlight

For the class
1   *model, Solar System (from Activity 10)
1 sht   *paper, plain
1 pair   *scissors
1 roll   tape, masking

*provided by the teacher

Preparation

1. Make a copy of Activity Sheet 11 for each student.

2. Insert two AA-size batteries into each penlight and two D-size batteries into each flashlight. Cut small pieces of white paper and tape them over the face of each flashlight and each penlight. Take care that the tape does not cover the face of the flashlight.

3. Each team of four will need a penlight and a flashlight.

Background Information

A *galaxy* is a swirling cluster of a multitude of stars. Many are spirals, shaped like gigantic pinwheels. Our Sun is but one of the estimated 100 billion stars in the *Milky Way* galaxy. Outside our galaxy, countless other galaxies stretch out through space, some larger and some smaller than ours. We refer to the vast space that surrounds the galaxies as well as all other existing matter and energy as the *universe.*

Because of the enormous distances from one object to another in the universe, scientists have developed a special unit to measure those distances—a *light-year*. A light-year is the distance light travels in 1 year, which is about 9.46 trillion km (5.88 trillion mi).

The Milky Way galaxy is about 100,000 light-years across. Proxima Centauri is the star in our galaxy closest to our Sun; it is 4.3 light-years away. (Proxima Centauri is the closest of a group of three stars that we call, collectively, Alpha Centauri.) In other words, light leaving Proxima Centauri at this moment will not arrive at Earth for 4.3 years.

The *relative brightness* of two stars viewed from Earth is not alone an accurate determination of their relative distance from Earth. A star's brightness also depends on its size, color, and temperature. Therefore, the brightest stars are not necessarily the closest stars.

Name _____ Activity Sheet 11

Star Light, Star Bright

How did the brightness of the penlight compare with the brightness of the flashlight when they were the same distance from you? Use the term *relative brightness* in your answer.
The relative brightness of the flashlight was greater.

How did the brightness of the penlight compare with the brightness of the flashlight when the penlight was closer to you?
The flashlight was still brighter.

How did the relative brightness of a penlight halfway across the classroom compare with a penlight at the far side of the classroom? Which light appeared to be brighter?
The closer penlight appeared to be brighter than the penlight farther away.

Can the relative brightness of a star be used as an indication of relative distance from Earth? Explain your answer.
Relative brightness should not be used as an indication of relative distance. Stars have different brightnesses, just as the flashlight and the penlight have different brightnesses. A star farther away than another may look closer because it is brighter.

Complete this sentence: A light-year is a measure of *distance.*

Star	Distance from Earth
Our Sun	8 seconds
Alpha Centauri	4.3 light-years
North Star (Polaris)	300 light-years
Rigel	1,000 light-years
Sirius	8.7 light-years
Betelgeuse	500 light-years

Which star is farther away, the North Star or Betelgeuse? *Betelgeuse*
Which star is closer, Alpha Centauri or Sirius? *Alpha Centauri*

Teaching Suggestions

1

Review the terms *star*, *sun*, and *solar system*. Remind students that our Sun is a star and that our Sun and all its satellites make up our Solar System.

Tell students that there are countless other stars in space besides our Sun and that they are very, very far away.

2

Write *North Star* and *Alpha Centauri* on the board. Tell students that these are two of the stars that will be discussed in this activity. Ask, **Do you know another name for the North Star?**

Ask students to recall the planet models they made in Activity 9. Ask, **What is the name of the imaginary line through the center of Earth?**

Ask, **What do we call the points on Earth at the ends of its axis?**

Additional Information

Some students may know that it is also called *Polaris*, or the *polestar*.

the axis

Many students will know that they are called the north and south poles.

Explain that the North Star, or Polaris, got its name because the axis of Earth at the north pole points toward that star. Travelers have used it for centuries as a guide in their journeys across land and oceans.

The North Star indicates the direction of north.

Begin a discussion of distances in space. Tell students that our star, the Sun, is a great distance from Earth, but that the next closest star is 272 times that distance from Earth! Write *149,600,000 km = Earth to Sun* on the board; under it, write *40,678,000,000 km = Earth to Alpha Centauri.*

Alpha Centauri is actually a triple-star system— three stars so closely related to one another that we refer to them as though they were a single star.

Bring students' attention to the classroom model of the Solar System. Ask, **What is the scaled distance from the Sun to Pluto?**

Some students may recall from Activity 8 that the distance between the model of the Sun and the model of Pluto is 6.6 m (about 20 ft). If students do not recall the scaled distance, have a volunteer measure it on the classroom model using a meterstick and report the figure to the rest of the class.

Tell students that, at the same scale used in the classroom model of the Solar System, a model of the North Star would have to be positioned out in space about 10 times as far away as our Moon.

Write the term *light-year* on the board. Tell students that because stars are so far away from Earth, astronomers use this special unit to describe the distances between them and other objects. A light-year is the distance that light travels in 1 year. A light-year is equal to 9.46 trillion kilometers (about 5.88 trillion miles).

Students may know that light travels very fast.

Explain that light leaving our Sun right now will not reach Earth for 8 seconds. Light leaving Alpha Centauri will not reach Earth for 4.3 years, and light leaving the North Star right now will not reach Earth for 300 years.

Star	Distance from Earth
Our Sun	8 seconds
Alpha Centauri	4.3 light years
North Star (Polaris)	300 light years
Rigel	1,000 light years
Sirius	8.7 light years
Betelgeuse	500 light years

Figure 11-1. Some stars and their distances from Earth.

Point out that many distant stars can be seen in the night sky. Ask, **Of all the stars you can see in the night sky, do you think the brightest stars are the closest stars to Earth?**

5 Accept all speculations.

Write *relative brightness* on the board. Tell students that they will experiment with lights to determine their relative brightness—whether one is brighter than another—at different distances, in order to discover the answer to this question.

6 Appoint two students (or ask for volunteers) to measure the classroom with a meterstick from one wall to the opposite wall. Have them divide the measurement by 2 in order to measure again to the point halfway across the classroom floor. Have them mark that distance with a long strip of masking tape.

7 Distribute a copy of Activity Sheet 11 to each student.

Group students by team along one wall of the classroom. Give a penlight to one member of each team and a flashlight to another member of the same team.

Tell the members of each team with lights to go to the opposite wall of the classroom and face their teammates. Tell them not to turn on the lights until instructed to do so.

8 Darken the room. Have the team members holding penlights and flashlights stand side by side. Tell them to turn their lights on, hold them steady, and shine the lights toward their teammates across the room. Their teammates are to observe the relative brightness of the two different lights.

Next, have the students holding flashlights stay where they are, flashlights turned on. Tell the students holding penlights to move to the center of the room (to the strip of masking tape) and again shine their penlights toward their teammates. Again, have their teammates observe the relative brightness of the two lights.

Finally, have pairs of team members swap tasks so that all students have the opportunity to hold the lights and to observe their relative brightness.

When all observations have been completed, tell students to complete their activity sheets. Tell them to record their observations, first comparing the brightness of two different lights at the same distance, then comparing the brightness of the two lights at different distances, and finally the brightness of two identical lights at different distances.

9

After students have completed their activity sheets, ask, **Do you think you can determine how far away a star is by how bright it is?**

10

No. Students should have observed that the flashlight was brighter than the penlight even when the flashlight was farther away.

Explain that all stars do not have the same actual brightness. Some stars are estimated to be 100,000 times brighter than our Sun. A star's actual brightness depends on its size and temperature.

Explain that even though the North Star is very bright in the sky, it is 300 light-years away from Earth.

Alpha Centauri is closer (4.3 light-years away), yet it is not as bright as the North Star.

Figure 11-2. Star light, star bright.

Tell students that scattered through space are massive, swirling clusters of billions of stars. Ask, **Do you know what such a huge cluster of stars is called?**

Write *galaxy* on the board. Explain that a galaxy is so huge that its stars are light-years away from each other.

Tell students that there are countless galaxies in space and that each galaxy consists of billions of stars.

11

Write *Milky Way* on the board. Explain that the Milky Way is the name of the galaxy to which our Solar System belongs.

12

Write *universe* on the board. Explain that the universe consists of all the galaxies and all the other matter and space around them.

Draw Figure 11-3 on the board to help students visualize the relationship between the universe, the galaxies, the stars, the planets, and the moons.

Ask, **If the universe contained trillions of galaxies and each galaxy contained billions of stars, how many stars would there be in the universe?**

More than anyone could count.

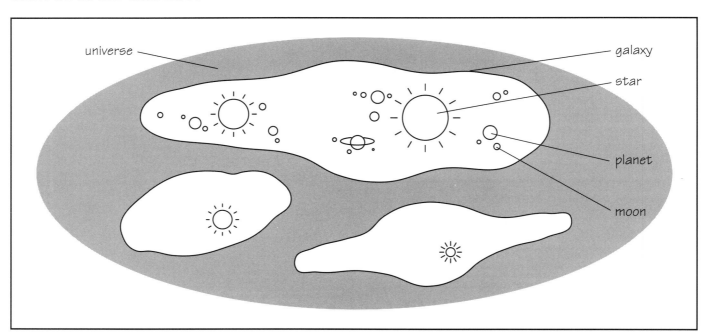

Figure 11-3. Stars, planets, and moons are located in galaxies. The universe consists of all the galaxies.

Reinforcement

Have students repeat the activity using only one type of light source (penlight or flashlight) but batteries of different strengths (old vs. new).

Cleanup

Have students return the penlights, flashlights, and roll of masking tape to the kit. (Remove the batteries from the penlights and flashlights before storing them in the kit.) Have students pull up and discard the strip of masking tape on the floor.

Connections

Science Challenge

Have each student inflate a small round balloon to the size of an orange and mark about 20 dots all over it with a black marking pen. Then have each student blow up the balloon while watching it in a mirror or watching a partner's balloon as it is inflated. (The dots will spread farther apart.) Explain that astronomers think the galaxies in the universe are spreading apart in the same way. One astronomer (Dr. Edwin Hubble, after whom the Hubble telescope is named) found that the farther from Earth a galaxy is, the faster it seems to be moving away.

Science Extension

Let students make a drawing of the listed stars using the scale 1 cm:1 light-year. To fit the farthest star listed (Rigel at 1,000 light-years), students will need a strip of paper slightly longer than 10 m (about 33 ft). Cut a strip of this length from a roll of white shelving paper or packaging paper for each team. You also may want to have teams work in a hallway, gym, or other large area.

The following activity demonstrates why stars seem to twinkle when viewed from Earth. Instruct teams as follows: Wrinkle a sheet of aluminum foil, put a glass bowl on it, and fill the bowl halfway with water. With the room darkened, shine a flashlight directly down on the water from a distance of about 30 cm (1 ft). Note the appearance of the foil viewed through the still water. Then gently tap the water surface with a pencil and observe the foil's appearance again. The water's movement bends the light reflected by the foil, causing it to blur and twinkle. Explain that in the same way, stars twinkle because their light rays are bent by moving air in Earth's atmosphere.

Science and Math

Tell students that astronomers have estimated that there are about 1,000 million galaxies in the universe and that each galaxy contains about 100,000 million stars. Ask students to use these estimates to calculate the number of stars in the universe. (100 million million million)

Science, Technology, and Society

Remind students of their star-twinkling investigation in the second Science Extension above. Explain that Earth's atmosphere also distorts images seen with telescopes on Earth's surface. In 1990, NASA launched the Hubble Space Telescope, the first telescope located in space beyond Earth's atmosphere. The Hubble telescope produces clear images of objects that are billions of light years from Earth. Encourage interested students to find out more about the Hubble Space Telescope, including successful efforts in December 1993 to correct flaws in some of its components. (A dramatic account of this repair mission, "The Big Fix" by John Dyson, is contained in the February 1995 issue of *Reader's Digest.*)

Tell students that about 3,000 years ago, Arabs invented and used an instrument called an *astrolabe* to navigate by the stars. Give teams the following instructions for making a simple model of an astrolabe: Tape one end of a 30-cm (1-ft) string to the center of a protractor's base and tie a metal washer or bolt to the other end. Lay a drinking straw along the protractor's base and tape it in place. To use the astrolabe, look through the straw at the top of a distant object, and have a partner note the angle of the string where it intersects the protractor's curve. Explain that by sighting on known stars, ancient navigators could determine their ship's location at sea.

Activity 12
Stories in the Sky

Objectives

In this activity students identify several of the constellations in the night sky. They make models of some of them and then write their own stories about how certain constellations might have gotten their names.

The students

- observe seasonal changes in the position of constellations as viewed from Earth

- construct constellation models and identify several constellations

- write a fictional story about the origin of a constellation

Schedule

About 50 minutes

Vocabulary

Big Dipper (Ursa Major, or Great Bear)
Cassiopeia
Cepheus
constellation
mythology
Orion (The Hunter)

Materials

For each student
1   Activity Sheet 12, Parts A and B

For each team of two
1	cardboard, square
1	push pin
1 pair	*scissors
1 roll	*transparent tape
1	tube, cardboard

For the class
2	bulbs, 100-watt
1	cardboard, square
1	Constellation Patterns
2 bottles	glue
2	light sources
1	*overhead projector
1 sht	paper, construction, black
1	push pin
1 pair	*scissors
4	transparencies (night sky in spring, summer, fall, and winter)
1	tube, cardboard

*provided by the teacher

Preparation

1. Make a copy of Activity Sheet 12, Parts A and B, for each student.

2. Make 17 copies of the Constellation Patterns, one for your demonstration model and one for each team.

3. Cut the sheet of black construction paper into 4-cm (about 1.6-in.) squares.

4. Partially prepare a demonstration viewer. Cut out one of the (reverse) constellation patterns, including its number. Place it in the center of a square of black construction paper and tape it in place temporarily with tiny pieces of transparent tape. With the cardboard square beneath the paper, punch out the pattern with a push pin through the black paper. Then put several beads of glue around one end of a cardboard tube. Place the square of black construction paper on the end with the glue, patterned side up. Stand the tube on the patterned end until the

glue dries. Finally, remove the tape and the pattern from the black paper.

5. Screw the bulbs into the light sources and choose two areas in the classroom where teams can share a light source. Have extension cords handy in case they are needed.

6. Each team of two will need one cardboard square, one push pin, one cardboard tube, one square of black construction paper, one copy of the Constellation Patterns, scissors, transparent tape, and access to the glue.

Background Information

Myths are stories passed down from ancient times. They depict both real and fictitious events, persons, and animals. Myths serve to recall significant events in the past or to explain people's practices, beliefs, or natural phenomena. *Mythology* is the study of myths.

Myths often involve the supernatural. When people did not know how to explain many natural events (earthquakes, eclipses, the changing seasons, and so on), they often attributed them to actions of beings who, they believed, resided in the sky. Patterns of stars that are visible in the night sky were often incorporated into the myths to represent certain beings and objects people thought were responsible for those mysterious events.

To create their sky-pictures, people somewhat arbitrarily grouped certain stars into patterns we now call *constellations*. Although constellations may comprise stars that are thousands of light-years apart, they appear to be on the same plane when viewed from Earth. Many of the 88 constellations we recognize today were originally named and described by the Greeks many centuries ago.

Some of the better-known constellations today are Aquarius, the Big Dipper (Ursa Major, or Great Bear), Cassiopeia, Cepheus, the Little Dipper (Ursa Minor, or Little Bear), and Orion (The Hunter).

Name _____   Activity Sheet 12, Part A

Stories in the Sky

1. Make your constellation viewer. Use a pattern and a push pin to make a constellation. Glue the square of black paper over one end of the tube and let the glue dry. Locate the number on the pattern. Write this number on the tube.

2. Point your constellation tube toward a light source and look through the tube. Match the pattern you see with one of the patterns shown below. Write the number that is on the tube below the pattern that matches it. Then write the name of the constellation next to the number.

1. Big Dipper   2. Cepheus   3. Cassiopeia   4. Orion

3. Swap viewers with a team whose viewer has a different number. View the constellation inside, and record the number and name of the constellation you see under its pattern above.

4. Swap viewers two more times until you have viewed all four constellations. Do not forget to record the number and name of each constellation you see under its pattern above.

Name _____   Activity Sheet 12, Part B

Stories in the Sky

Recall that myths are stories of great adventures or unexplainable events that happened long ago. Imagine that you are a story writer, gazing at the night sky. Choose a constellation and give it a new name. Then develop your own myth about how that constellation got its name. Be sure to include names and descriptions of characters. Draw the constellation too.

Teaching Suggestions	Additional Information

1

Remind students what they learned in Activity 11—that there are countless stars in the universe, that they are enormous distances apart from one another, and that our Sun is one of those stars.

Ask, **How could you describe some of the stars you have seen in the night sky?**

Accept descriptions of single stars as well as combinations and patterns of stars.

2

Write the word *constellation* on the board. Explain that a constellation is a particular area of the sky that contains a particular set of stars. If imaginary lines were drawn to connect the stars in a constellation, the resulting shape might resemble a person, an animal, or an object.

Display the transparency of the night sky in winter. Locate the constellation Orion near the southern horizon and trace its shape with your finger. Tell students that these stars always appear in the same arrangement and that this constellation is called *Orion.*

Project the image onto the ceiling, if possible, with your projector.

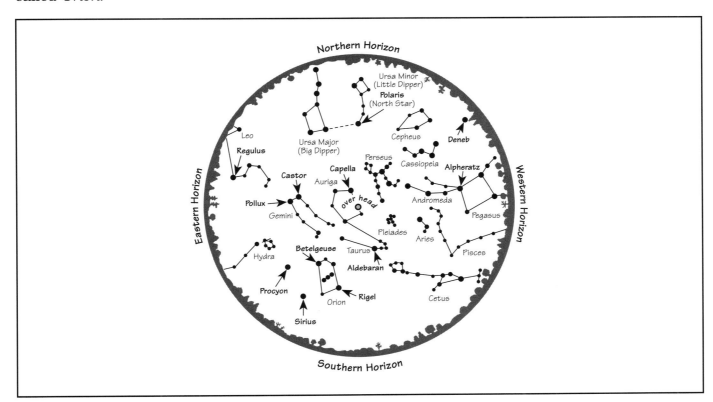

Figure 12-1. The night sky in winter.

Point out the names of two of the stars that make up this constellation—Betelgeuse and Rigel. Ask, **Are these stars the same distance from Earth?**

No. Students may remember that they learned in Activity 11 that Betelgeuse is 500 light-years away and Rigel is almost 1,000 light-years away.

Remind students that comparing stars' brightness is not a good indication of their relative distance from Earth. Even though the two stars in this constellation appear to be about the same distance away from us, their distances from Earth are actually light-years apart.

Begin a discussion of how constellations got their names. Tell students that many constellations were named after imaginary characters, animals, and objects. A constellation might represent a swan, a ram, a fish, a big bear, a little bear, and so on.

Write the word *mythology* on the board. Explain that mythology is the study of myths, which are stories from ancient times. These stories tell of real and imaginary (even supernatural) events, persons, and animals.

Students may have heard of Hercules, a mythological hero with supernatural strength.

Remind students that there are four seasons in a year—spring, summer, fall, and winter. Display the overhead transparency of the constellations of the night sky in spring. Locate the Big Dipper (Ursa Major), near the center of the transparency, and trace the constellation's shape with your finger.

Identify this constellation as the Big Dipper and point out that it is shaped like a long-handled cup that is used to dip up water for drinking.

Make sure all students are able to see and identify the shape of the constellation.

Next, display the transparency showing the night sky in summer. Point out that the Big Dipper is in a different part of the sky during this season.

Explain to students that the stars making up a constellation always form the same shape but that from our viewpoint on Earth their positions in the night sky change through the year.

Ask, **What do you know about Earth's orbit around the Sun that could explain why this happens?**

Tell students that Earth's revolution around the Sun causes our view of the night sky to change through the seasons, until constellations return to their original positions after an entire year.

Identify several other constellations, such as Cepheus in the summer sky and Cassiopeia in the transparency of the night sky in fall.

Explain that there are more than 88 other recognized constellations and that almost every one has its own story based on myth.

Tell students that they will make their own constellation viewers. Ask for their attention while you demonstrate how to assemble one.

Show them your demonstration tube with the paper square glued to it. Tell teams they will each cut out one of the constellation patterns, including its number, place it over a square of black construction paper and tape it in place temporarily with tiny pieces of transparent tape. Tell them they will then place the piece of paper on the cardboard square and punch out the pattern with a push pin through the black paper.

Next, they will put several beads of glue around one end of a cardboard tube and then place the square of black construction paper on the end with the glue, patterned side up. They should then stand the tube on the patterned end until the glue dries. Finally, they should carefully remove the tape and the pattern from the black paper.

Choose one of the reverse constellation patterns. Show students how to lay the pattern face-up on the black construction paper and, using the cardboard as a base, poke holes with the push pin through the dots on the pattern and through the black construction paper.

Encourage answers that indicate that students are familiar with the concepts of Earth's revolution around the Sun and the enormous distance it travels in one orbit.

Earth's rotation causes the stars to appear to make a complete circle around the planet once a day.

5

Observant students may notice that the constellation pattern is reversed. Tell them this is necessary so that the pattern will have the correct orientation when viewed through the tube.

Tell students that they are to find the number that appears next to each pattern and write it on the tube. Explain that the number will be used later to identify the name of the constellation.

Give a copy of Activity Sheet 12, Part A, to each student. Distribute a cardboard square, a push pin, a cardboard tube, a square of black construction paper, a copy of the Constellation Patterns, transparent tape, and scissors to each team of two. Have each team gather around one of the two light sources.

Assign each team one of the four constellation patterns to cut out and use for their viewers.

With your demonstration tube, go to one of the light sources and show students how you hold the tube with the patterned end toward the light while you look through the tube at the bright constellation pattern.

Tell students to construct their constellation viewers, look through them toward the light sources, and then complete their activity sheets.

Leave the transparency of the night sky in winter projected so that students can identify the patterns they see in their tubes.

Tell teams they will swap constellation tubes with other teams until all students

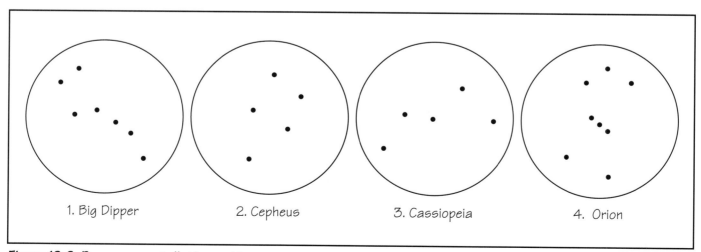

1. Big Dipper   2. Cepheus   3. Cassiopeia   4. Orion

Figure 12-2. Reverse constellation patterns.

have identified the four constellation patterns and recorded the names on their activity sheets.

After teams have completed their activity sheets, call their attention to the board.

Write the numbers and names of the constellations on the board: *1, Big Dipper; 2, Cepheus; 3, Cassiopeia; 4, Orion.*

Also refer to Figure 12-2.

Have teams check their answers on their activity sheets with the key on the board to confirm that they named the constellations correctly.

Tell students that next they will write their own story about any constellation that they choose. Project one or more of the transparencies for students to observe various constellations again.

As an example, tell students that in Greek mythology Orion was known as The Hunter. He was the son of Poseidon. He is seen in the stars holding a shield in his left hand and a club in his right. His right shoulder is represented by one of the largest stars known—Betelgeuse. Rigel and Salph represent his two feet. Three bright stars make up his belt. You could also tell the story about how the constellation Cassiopeia got its name. In Greek mythology, Cassiopeia was a queen of Ethiopia. She was to be killed by a monster sent by Poseidon, but she was saved by Perseus. Her constellation represents the form of a woman seated in a chair, holding up her arms.

Distribute a copy of Activity Sheet 12, Part B, to each student.

When all the stories are written, ask volunteers to share their stories with the class. Call attention to parts of stories that involve Earth and other objects in our Solar System as well as other stars.

Reinforcement

Have each student draw his or her constellation on chart paper for display in the classroom. If appropriate, students may use their constellation viewers to teach other students in the school about constellations.

Cleanup

Light sources, push pins, bottles of glue, and cardboard squares should be returned to the kit. Transparencies and the Constellation Patterns should be replaced in the kit. Have students discard paper scraps and used copies of constellation patterns. Team members may want to take turns taking their constellation viewers home.

Science at Home

Encourage students to teach someone at home about the constellations. Tell them to use a flashlight to point out stars and constellations in the night sky. The shaft of light from a flashlight works remarkably well to point out specific stars and shapes of constellations at night. Particles of dust and moisture in the air reflect the light along the path of the beam, making it quite visible.

Connections

Science Challenge

Have pairs of students do the following activity during the viewing session suggested below: Cut a string 30 cm (1 ft) longer than your height and tie a nail to one end so the nail points downward. Lay a large sheet of poster paper on the ground. Loop the free end of the string around your index finger, then stand at one edge of the paper and point to a star in the Big Dipper. Your partner should mark the spot on the paper directly below the nail point. Continue pointing to different stars in the Big Dipper while your partner marks the nail's position for each one. When all stars are plotted, a large drawing of the Big Dipper will be formed on the paper. Find and mark the position of the North Star by drawing a straight line that connects the two stars in the right edge of the dipper's bowl and projects beyond it to the North Star.

Science Extension

Arrange at least one evening viewing session (chaperoned by parents or other volunteers) for the class to observe the night sky. For the best viewing, choose a moonless night. Help students locate several constellations and the planets that can be seen with the naked eye (Mercury, Venus, Mars, Jupiter, and Saturn). If you are not adept at locating constellations and planets yourself, consult children's astronomy guides such as *Sky Detective* by Eileen M. Docekal (Sterling, 1992) and *Astronomy* by Peter Lafferty (Marshall Cavendish, 1989) before and during the viewing session, and try to find at least one chaperone who can also help students. If possible, obtain several pairs of binoculars or a telescope so students can observe the planets more closely.

Before the viewing session described above, have each student make a device called a "star frame" to help focus on one particular group of stars at a time. Make a star frame yourself as a demonstration: Bend a wire coat hanger into a square by pulling on the middle of the long bottom wire. Bend the hook and wrap it with tape to make a handle. Show students how to hold up the star frame at arm's length to view the sky in sections.

Science and the Arts

Ask students to find pictures of constellations in astronomy guides and other books. Have each student choose a favorite constellation and mark its stars with white paint on a large sheet of dark blue or black construction paper, then use colored paints, chalk, or other materials of his or her choice to draw the figure represented in the constellation.

Science and Language Arts

Encourage students to read myths about the Greek and Roman gods whose names were given to planets and constellations. You may want to do this as a cooperative learning activity, with a different god assigned to each team and students preparing a report that includes a short tale about the god's exploits. Give each team an opportunity to present its report to the rest of the class.

Science and Social Studies

Encourage students to find out about the sky myths developed by other cultures besides the Greeks and Romans. For example, the Tsimshians, Native Americans of the Pacific Northwest, believed that the Sun—whom they called "The One Who Walks Over the Sky"—wears a flaming mask that lights Earth and creates stars with sparks blowing out of his mouth when he sleeps. (This and other myths can be found in *Sky Detective*, cited above.)

Assessment

Objectives

Students are given three different ways to demonstrate their understanding of the material presented in Solar System.

The students

■ use a drawing compass to draw a circle

■ construct a device to draw an ellipse

■ describe why planets have elliptical orbits

■ calculate the scale model diameters of the planets and the Sun, given their actual diameters and the scale

■ draw to scale and label a planet in the Solar System

■ draw and label the parts of a solar system

■ show how the parts of the universe are related to each other

■ identify a meteor and describe how it differs from an asteroid and a comet

■ explain why constellations appear to move from month to month

■ describe how to build a scale model

■ devise a mnemonic device to remember the nine planets in their correct order

Schedule

About 60 minutes; 20 minutes for each section

Materials

For each student

1	Assessment Activity Sheets 1, 2, and 3, Parts A and B

1	*pencil

For the class

11	cardboard, square, 34 cm x 34 cm
11	compasses, drawing
33 sht	*paper, plain
22	push pins
11	rulers, metric
1 pair	*scissors
1 roll	string
1 roll	tape, masking

*provided by teacher

Preparation

1. Make a copy of Assessment Activity Sheets 1, 2, and 3, Parts A and B, for each student. Make one copy of the Assessment Summary Chart for the class.

2. Place a sheet of plain paper in the center of each of the 11 cardboard squares. Tape down the corners. Place one square at each station.

3. Cut eleven 25-cm (about 10-in.) lengths of string. Tie the ends of the string in a secure knot to form a loop. Stretched out, the loop should measure no more than 10 cm (about 4 in.). Trim off ends of the string above the knot. Place one string loop at each station.

4. Place one drawing compass, one metric ruler, and two push pins at each station as well.

5. Plan how to divide the class into three groups. Group one will start at the hands-on stations. Groups two and three will need desks or tables at which to work. Every student will need a pencil.

Background Information

This multi-dimensional assessment is designed to measure students' understanding more thoroughly than traditional tests. Section 1 assesses students' mastery through hands-on tasks; Section 2, through picture interpretation; and Section 3, through verbal problem solving and questions.

Assessment Instructions

1 Tell students that the purpose of the upcoming activities is to provide three ways to assess some of what they have learned from the module.

Divide the class into three groups. Assign one group Section 1 of the assessment; the second group, Section 2; and the third group, Section 3. Distribute the appropriate activity sheets to each group.

Students participating in Section 1 should move to the prepared hands-on stations. Explain that all equipment needed to complete Section 1 is provided at the stations.

Students in groups two and three should follow the instructions on their activity sheets.

> Name _____ Assessment Activity Sheet 1, Part A
>
> ## Assessment – Section 1
>
> **1.** Use your ruler and pencil to measure and draw a 20-cm (8-in.) line lengthwise down the center of the paper. Make a dot at the midpoint of the line. Label the dot S. Draw a circle with a 5-cm radius whose focus is at S. Label it *Shape A*. What is the circle's diameter?
>
> 10 cm
> How did you figure that out?
> The diameter is twice the radius of the circle.

2 Students working at hands-on stations to complete Section 1 will be drawing circles and ellipses, then describing why a planet's orbit is in the shape of an ellipse, rather than a circle.

When all groups have finished, collect their Assessment Activity Sheets. Instruct students at the hands-on stations to remove the push pins from the cardboard and leave them at the station. Have them remove their drawing from the cardboard and dispose of it. Replenish each piece of cardboard with a fresh sheet of paper. Take care to move the paper location slightly so the same push pin holes are not used by more than one student. Make sure that the drawing compasses are functioning properly, and that strings are still tied securely.

Rotate the groups and assign Assessment Section 1 to group two, Section 2 to group three, and Section 3 to group one. Have group two trade places with group one at the hands-on stations.

Repeat this procedure until all students have completed all three sections.

Name _____ Assessment Activity Sheet 1, Part B

Assessment – Section 1

2. Make two more dots on the line—at the two points where the line and the circle meet. Press push pins into the dots, leaving just enough space so the string can move freely underneath them.

3. Place the string loop around the push pins. Insert the pencil tip into the loop and pull gently so that the string does not droop. What shape do you predict that you will be making if you move the pencil around the two push pins?
an ellipse

4. Keeping gentle pressure on the loop of string, draw a line as you move the pencil around the two push pins. Label the shape your line traces *Shape B*. What shape did you produce?
an ellipse

Was your prediction correct?
Answers will vary.

In our Solar System, which objects follow this sort of path around the Sun?
planets

What is this path called?
an orbit

Why isn't the path a perfect circle?
The planet in its orbit experiences the
gravitational pull of many different objects in the
Solar System.

Name _____ Assessment Activity Sheet 2, Part A

Assessment – Section 2

1. The chart below shows the names of the planets, as well as their actual diameters. Using a scale of 1 cm:10,000 km, calculate the scale model diameters, and enter them in the third column (three are already completed for you).

Name	Actual Diameter (km)	Scale Model Diameter (cm) Scale = 1 cm:10,000 km
Sun	1,392,000	139.2
Mercury	4,878	0.5
Venus	12,100	1.2
Earth	12,756	1.3
Mars	6,786	0.7
Jupiter	143,200	14.3
Saturn	120,536	12.1
Uranus	51,118	5.1
Neptune	49,528	5.0
Pluto	2,400	0.24

Using the zero mark on the ruler below as the focus of your planet circle, draw and label one planet to scale. Draw your planet freehand.

Neptune

Why are scale models helpful?
You can better visualize the relative sizes of the
planets if you are able to see them all on one
sheet of paper.

Name _____ Assessment Activity Sheet 2, Part B

Assessment – Section 2

2. A solar system is made up of a star and all the objects that travel around it. Based on this definition, create your own solar system in the space below. Make sure that you label everything you draw, including the paths of the orbits around the star.

3. Draw a sketch or write a paragraph about how the space terms below are related to each other. (Hint—the universe is the largest object.)

Planet   Galaxy   Star   Universe   Moon

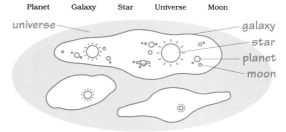

Name _____   Assessment Activity Sheet 3, Part A

Assessment – Section 3

1. Michael, Juan and Dee Dee stared up at the sky on a clear, moonless night. Suddenly, a white light shot across the sky, with no tail trailing behind. Michael stated that it was a meteor. Juan thought that it was an asteroid and Dee Dee said it was a comet. Who was correct and why?

Michael was correct—it was a meteor, a meteoroid burning and glowing as it is pulled toward Earth's atmosphere. An asteroid is a very small, rocky planet. If an asteroid were pulled into a planet's atmosphere, it would burn, becoming a meteor. A comet is a small, icy, rocky mass. As its orbit approaches the Sun, the ice begins to melt. Particles that break free from the ice form a long tail behind the comet, and its particles reflect sunlight, which appear as a tail to us.

Dee Dee added that if they looked up at the same spot in three months, the constellations would be in an entirely different part of the sky. Using the term *revolution*, explain why Dee Dee is right.

The Earth's revolution around the Sun causes our view of the night sky to change from month to month. After one year, the constellations return to their original positions.

Name _____   Assessment Activity Sheet 3, Part B

Assessment – Section 3

2. Anthony wants to build a scale model of his town. What information does he need to know before he starts his project? What must he decide before he lays out his "town"? Use the terms *scale*, *ratio* and *relative size* in your response.

Anthony must first find out the actual size of the objects in his town, and then determine the size he wants his scale town to be. Once he finds out both pieces of information, he can calculate the scale, or ratio, he will be using. Once his scale model is complete, he can better visualize the relative size of the objects in his town.

3. You learned a trick (called a *mnemonic device*) to help remember the names of the planets in order of their distance from the Sun. One of the sentences was "Many Very Energetic Moms Join Some Unique New Programs," which helped you to remember that the nine planets are Mercury, Venus, Earth, Mars, Jupiter, Saturn, Uranus, Neptune, and Pluto. Think of a sentence of your own that will help you remember the planets in their correct order.

Students may answer as their imaginations dictate.

Scoring

Answers are printed on the reduced Assessment Activity Sheets on this and the preceding pages. However, in some cases, various answers are appropriate. An example of a reasonable answer for each open-ended question is given, but students may think of other, equally appropriate responses.

The Assessment Summary Chart allows you to summarize class and individuals' mastery of skills and concepts, and to show parents or principals the students' accomplishments.

 Scoring Key for Assessment Summary Chart

○ not appropriate or gave no answer

✓ appropriate but gave one or more incorrect answers

● appropriate and gave no incorrect answer(s)

For each student, one of the above symbols should be entered in each column of the Assessment Summary Chart.

Glossary

aphelion The point along a planet's orbit at which it is farthest from the Sun.

asteroid One of millions of very small planets that orbit the Sun.

asteroid belt The area between the orbits of Mars and Jupiter where most of the asteroids in our Solar System are concentrated.

axis An imaginary line, or axle, through the center of an object, about which the object rotates.

circle A closed curved line on which all points are equidistant from its center.

circumference The length of the closed curve of a circle.

comet A mass of ice-covered dust and rock particles that orbits the Sun or a planet.

constellation An area of the sky containing stars that seem to outline a figure, as viewed from Earth.

crater The bowl-shaped depression in the surface of a satellite caused by the impact of a meteorite.

day The length of time a planet takes to make one complete rotation about its axis.

diameter The distance from one side of a circle, through the focus, to the other side.

Earth The third planet from the Sun in our Solar System.

ellipse A shape like a flattened circle.

focus (plural: foci) The point at the center of a circle.

force A push or pull on an object.

friction The rubbing together of two substances.

galaxy One of countless swirling, massive clusters of solar systems in the universe.

gravity The attractive force that exists between objects.

Jupiter The fifth planet from the Sun in our Solar System.

light-year A unit of distance, equal to the distance light travels in a year—about 9.46 trillion km.

map A scale drawing used to represent geographic locations and their relative distances from one another.

Mars The fourth planet from the Sun in our Solar System.

mass The measure of the amount of material an object contains.

Mercury The planet closest to the Sun in our Solar System.

meteor A meteoroid falling though a planet's atmosphere and burning brightly because of friction.

meteorite The part of a meteor that crashes into the surface of a satellite.

meteoroid One of countless bits of rock and metal, smaller than asteroids, that orbit the Sun or a planet.

Milky Way The galaxy of which our Solar System is a member.

mnemonic device A memory aid, such as a made-up sentence or rhyme, that helps recall the order of items in a list.

moon A satellite of a planet.

Neptune The eighth planet from the Sun in our Solar System.

North Star (Polaris) The star almost directly above the north pole of the Earth.

orbit The elliptical path that a satellite travels as it moves around the Sun or a planet.

perihelion The point along a planet's orbit at which it is nearest to the Sun.

planet A large, spherical satellite of a star.

Pluto The ninth planet from the Sun in our Solar System.

radius (plural: radii) The distance on a circle from the focus to the circumference.

ratio A numerical representation of a relationship between two measurements, as in a scale for a drawing or a model.

relative brightness The brightness of an object when compared with the brightness of surrounding objects.

relative distance The distance between objects when compared with the distance between surrounding objects.

relative size The size of an object when compared with the size of surrounding objects.

revolution One complete orbit of a satellite.

rotation One complete turn of a satellite about its axis.

satellite An object in orbit around a larger object.

Saturn The sixth planet from the Sun in our Solar System.

scale A proportion used in determining the relationship between two measurements of size or distance.

scale drawing A two-dimensional scaled representation of a smaller or larger object.

solar system A star and all the satellites that orbit it.

star An extremely large, hot ball of burning gas that radiates light and heat.

Sun The star of our Solar System.

system An interdependent group of items that form a unified whole.

universe The vast space that surrounds and includes all the galaxies as well as all other existing matter and energy.

Uranus The seventh planet from the Sun in our Solar System.

Venus The second planet from the Sun in our Solar System.

year The length of time a planet takes to make one complete revolution around the Sun.

References and Resources

Books

Astronomy
Kristen Lippincott. Dorling Kindersley, 1994.

Astronomy
Philip Steele. Silver Burdett, 1991.

Astronomy Smart Junior: The Science of the Solar System and Beyond
Michael L. Bentley (Princeton Review Series). Princeton Review, 1996.

Big Bang: The Story of the Universe
Heather Couper and Nigel Henbest. DK Publishing, 1997.

Comets, Meteors, and Asteroids
Seymour Simon. Morrow, 1994.

Earth, Moon and Sun
Delta Education, Inc., 1994.

Facts on File Atlas of Stars and Planets
Ian Ridpath. Facts on File, 1993.

The Illustrated World of Space
Iain Nicolson. Simon and Schuster, 1991.

Janice VanCleave's Astronomy for Every Kid: 101 Easy Experiments that Really Work
Janice VanCleave. Wiley, 1991.

The Kingfisher Young People's Book of Space
Martin Redfern. Kingfisher, 1998.

Let's Investigate Science: The Solar System
Robin Kerrod. Marshall Cavendish, 1995.

The Magic School Bus Lost in the Solar System
Joanna Cole. Scholastic, 1992.

Our Solar System
Seymour Simon. Morrow, 1992.

Our Solar System
Peter Riley, Jeremy Pyke, Nick Hawken (Illustrator), and Lawrence T. Lorimer. Readers Digest, 1998.

Solar Energy (Delta Science Module)
Delta Education, 1994.

Stars and Planets
David H. Levy (The Nature Company Discoveries Library). Time-Life, 1996.

Stars, Clusters, and Galaxies
John R. Gustafson. Silver Burdett, 1993.

Story of the Universe
David Hughes. Troll, 1991.

The Third Planet: Exploring the Earth from Space
Sally Ride and Tam O'Shaughnessy. Crown Publishers, 1994.

The Usborne Complete Book of Astronomy and Space
Lisa Miles and Alastair Smith. Usborne/EDC Publishing.

Voyager: An Adventure to the Edge of the Solar System
Sally Ride. Crown, 1992.

Voyager to the Planets
Necia H. Apfel. Houghton Mifflin, 1994.

The Young Oxford Book of Astronomy
Simon and Jacqueline Milton. Oxford University Press, 1995.

Zero Gravity
Gloria Skurzynski. Simon and Schuster, 1994.

Software

The Great Solar System Rescue (CD-ROM or Videodisc)
Tom Snyder Productions.
Web Site: www.teachtsp.com

Meet Our Solar System

What is a solar system? _____

_____

_____

_____

What is the name of the star in our Solar System? _____

What are the parts of our Solar System?

_____

How many planets are there in our Solar System? _____

What are the names of the planets in our Solar System, in order
beginning with the planet closest to the Sun?

_____

_____

_____

_____

_____

_____

_____

_____

1. Cut each strip of blue construction paper into three pieces, two
   9-cm pieces and one 10-cm piece. With a black marker, write the
   name of one planet lengthwise on each strip of paper. Use the
   longest pieces for the longest names.

2. On Part B of the activity sheet, beginning next to the curve that
   represents the edge of the Sun, arrange your nine labels in the
   order of each planet's distance from the Sun, just as your teacher
   did on the board. Glue your labels to the page under the numbers
   1 to 9.

Meet Our Solar System

1   2   3   4   5   6   7   8   9

Sun

Earth Orbits the Sun

1. Make a satellite system model like the one shown below. Tie one end of the fishing line to the washer. Thread the other end of the line through the tube and then through the hole in the ball. Tie this end around the ball. Hold the washer next to the bottom of the tube, raise your fist above your head and begin rotating your fist so that the ball circles your fist.

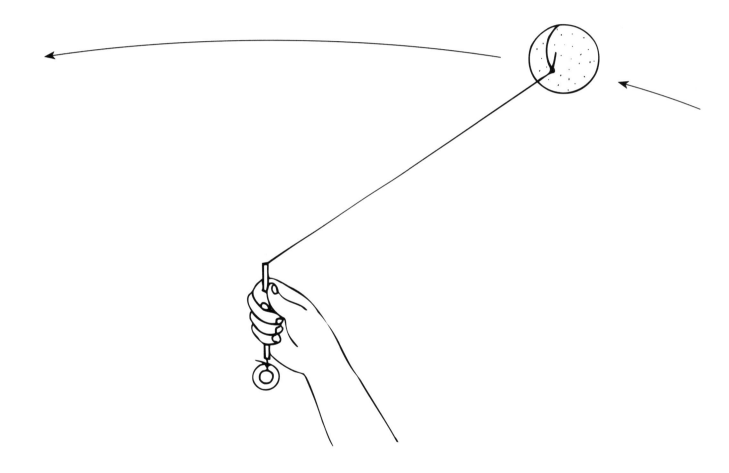

What is the satellite in this model? _____

What is the satellite orbiting? _____

2. Imagine that this is a model of our Solar System.
What object is represented by your fist? _____

3. Imagine that this is a model of our Solar System.
What object is represented by the ball? _____

Orbits Are Not Circles

1. Use your pencil and ruler to measure and draw a line lengthwise down the center of the paper. Measure and make a dot at the mid-point of the line. Label this dot C. Put a push pin in dot C and then put the string loop under the push pin. Put your pencil in the string loop and gently pull. Draw a circle as shown in the diagram below.

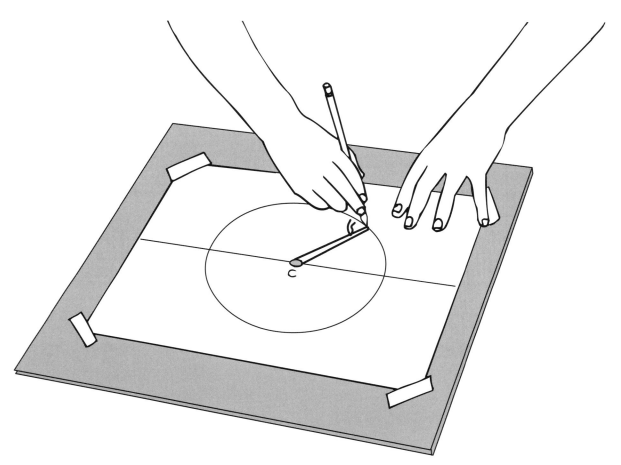

© 1996 Delta Education, Inc. Permission granted to purchaser to photocopy for classroom use.

2. Measure and put two more dots on the line, each 4 cm (about 1.6 in.) from C. Label one S and the other X. Move the push pin from C to X. Place another push pin in S. Put the string loop around and under both push pins. Draw an ellipse with the setup.

What is the term for the point in a planet's orbit when the planet is farthest from the Sun? _____

What is the term for the point in a planet's orbit when the planet is closest to the Sun? _____

What is the term for the shape of a planet's orbit? _____

Making Circles

What is the radius of the circle drawn in Activity 3? _____

What is the diameter of that same circle? _____

1. Tape a sheet of paper to the cardboard. Draw a dot near the center of the paper. Label the dot *C*. Put the point of the compass into the dot labeled *C*, as shown in the illustration below.

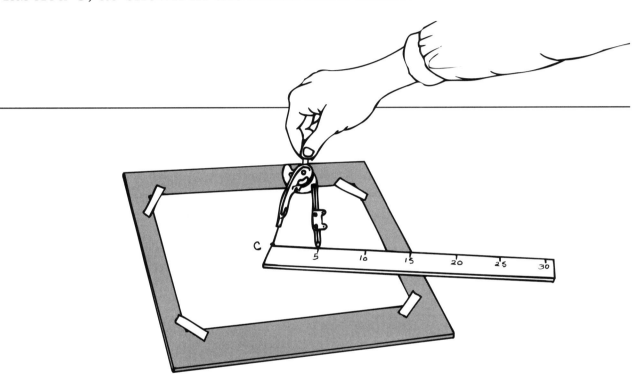

2. Use the compass to draw a circle that has a radius of 5 cm. Use your ruler to measure. What is the diameter of this circle? _____

3. Make two circles—one with a radius of 3 cm and the other with a radius of 10 cm.

What is the diameter of the circle with a 3-cm radius? _____

What is the diameter of the circle with a 10-cm radius? _____

4. Label the radius of each circle with the word *radius.*

Do you see a relationship between the lengths of a radius and a diameter in each circle? Explain.

_____

_____

Scale and Relative Size

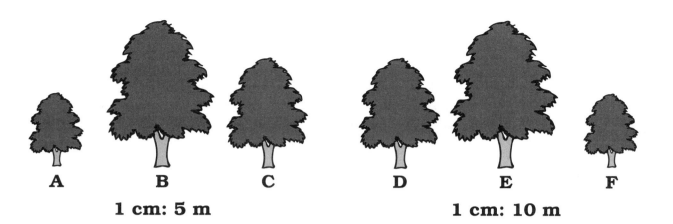

A   **B**   **C**   **D**   **E**   **F**

1 cm: 5 m   **1 cm: 10 m**

Measure the height of each drawing of a tree. Record your measurement of the drawing in the chart below. Then calculate the heights of the actual trees.

	Tree A	Tree B	Tree C	Tree D	Tree E	Tree F
Drawing Height (cm)						
Actual Height (m)						

What is the scale used to draw Trees A, B, and C? _____

What is the scale used to draw Trees D, E, and F? _____

Is the drawing of Tree A the same height as the drawing of Tree F? _____

Is the actual height of Tree A the same as the actual height of Tree F? Why or why not?

_____

If the drawings are the same heights, but the scales to which they were drawn are different, are the actual heights of the trees the same or different? _____

How could you tell which actual tree is taller if you have two drawings that are the same heights but have been drawn to different scales? (Hint: Compare the scale ratios.)

_____

_____

Modeling Planet Sizes

How can you make models of the planets that allow you to compare their relative sizes?

_____

_____

_____

Name	Actual Diameter (km)	Scale Model Diameter (cm) Scale = 1 cm:5000 km	Scale Model Radius (cm) Scale = 1 cm:5000 km
Sun	1,392,000		
Mercury	4,878	1.0	
Venus	12,100	2.4	
Earth	12,756	2.6	
Mars	6,786	1.4	
Jupiter	143,200	28.6	
Saturn	120,536	24.1	
Uranus	51,118	10.2	
Neptune	49,528	9.9	
Pluto	2,400	0.5	

1. Calculate each scale model radius from the scale model diameters given above. Record the radius in the Scale Model Radius column.

2. Use the Scale Model Radius measurements to measure, draw, and cut out circles. The circles representing Mercury, Mars, and Pluto will be too small to measure with the drawing compass. Use the ruler to measure these three planets and draw the circles by hand.

3. Write the names of the four largest planets on strips of masking tape with the black marker and then attach the labels to those models. Make tape "handles" for the five smallest planets, as shown on the board. Write their names on the tape handles.

List the planets according to relative size. Start with the largest and finish with the smallest.

_____

_____

Scale and Relative Distance

1. Measure from the book (on the floor by the board) to your desk, from the book to the teacher's desk, and from the book to the wall opposite the board.

   What are the actual distances?

   _____   _____   _____

2. Decide on a scale that will enable you to reduce the distances so that you can draw the relative distances in the space below. (Hint: First take the longest distance and scale it down to fit.)

   What scale did you use? _____

   What are the scaled distances?

   _____   _____   _____

3. Make your scale drawing below. Measure and mark off in centimeters the scaled distances to each object. Make an ✗ to represent each object and label the ✗s.

Modeling Planet Distances

What do you know about the shape of a planet's orbit that makes it necessary to use the planet's average distance from the Sun as a measurement in the chart below? Use the terms *perihelion* and *aphelion* in your answer.

_____

_____

_____

_____

Planet	Average Actual Distance from Sun (km)	Scale Model Distance from Sun (cm) Scale = 1 cm:9,000,000 km
Mercury	57,800,000	6.4
Venus	108,200,000	12.0
Earth	149,600,000	16.6
Mars	227,900,000	25.3
Jupiter	778,300,000	86.5
Saturn	1,429,400,000	158.8
Uranus	2,871,000,000	319.0
Neptune	4,501,200,000	500.0
Pluto	6,000,000,000	666.6

Refer to the chart above for the scaled distance from the Sun of each planet's orbit. On the model of the Solar System, measure out from the Sun the scaled distance for your assigned planet and make a dot on the paper. Position your planet model so that its center is over the dot. Tape your planet model in place on the paper.

Which two planets have their orbits between Earth and the Sun?

_____

Which two planets orbit at the greatest distance from the Sun?

_____

Days and Years

1. Complete these sentences:

A day is the time it takes a planet to complete one _____ about its axis.

A year is the time it takes a planet to complete one _____ around the Sun.

2. Disassemble the satellite model. Put the plastic tube into the hole in the foam ball so that the ends of the tube stick out on both sides of the ball. This is your Earth model. Use one end of the tube as a handle and spin the ball as you would you spin a top.

As you spin the model, are you simulating days or years? _____

3. Go to one of the light sources. Hold the Earth model by the tube and near the light. Rotate the ball once.

What do you notice about how much of the model is lit and how much is dark?

_____

Do the sizes of the light and dark areas change when you rotate the Earth model? _____

What do the light and dark areas represent on Earth?

_____

4. Continue to hold the model by the tube, but now move the ball around the light source. What are you simulating now, a day or a year? _____

5. Make one revolution with your model close to the light source. Now, move the model farther away from the light source and make another revolution, moving the model at the same speed.

Which revolution took longer? _____

_____

If planets have orbits of different sizes, will all planets make one revolution in the same length of time? _____

Does a planet with a very large orbit take more time to make one revolution around the Sun? If so, which planet has the longest year? _____

Asteroids, Meteoroids, and Comets

1. Make 8–10 dots along the elliptical orbit to represent the comet at different points of its orbit. Label the perihelion and the aphelion of the comet's orbit.

2. Draw in each of the comets' tails. Remember that a comet's tail always points away from the Sun. Label the head and tail of one of the drawings. Color the comets.

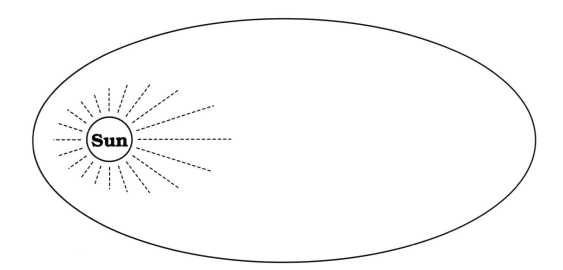

Star Light, Star Bright

How did the brightness of the penlight compare with the brightness of the flashlight when they were the same distance from you? Use the term *relative brightness* in your answer.

_____

How did the brightness of the penlight compare with the brightness of the flashlight when the penlight was closer to you?

_____

How did the relative brightness of a penlight halfway across the classroom compare with a penlight at the far side of the classroom? Which light appeared to be brighter?

_____

_____

Can the relative brightness of a star be used as an indication of relative distance from Earth? Explain your answer.

_____

_____

_____

_____

_____

Complete this sentence: A light-year is a measure of _____

Star	Distance from Earth
Our Sun	8 seconds
Alpha Centauri	4.3 light-years
North Star (Polaris)	300 light-years
Rigel	1,000 light-years
Sirius	8.7 light-years
Betelgeuse	500 light-years

Which star is farther away, the North Star or Betelgeuse? _____

Which star is closer, Alpha Centauri or Sirius? _____

Stories in the Sky

1. Make your constellation viewer. Use a pattern and a push pin to make a constellation. Glue the square of black paper over one end of the tube and let the glue dry. Locate the number on the pattern. Write this number on the tube.

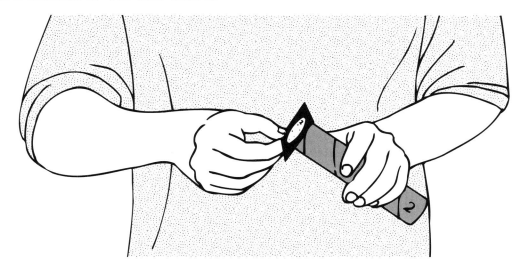

2. Point your constellation tube toward a light source and look through the tube. Match the pattern you see with one of the patterns shown below. Write the number that is on the tube below the pattern that matches it. Then write the name of the constellation next to the number.

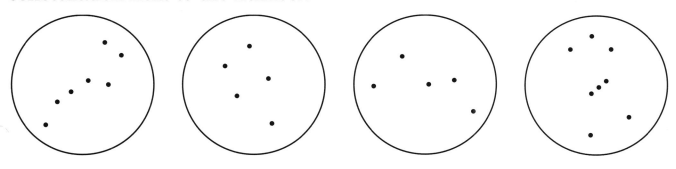

3. Swap viewers with a team whose viewer has a different number. View the constellation inside, and record the number and name of the constellation you see under its pattern above.

4. Swap viewers two more times until you have viewed all four constellations. Do not forget to record the number and name of each constellation you see under its pattern above.

Stories in the Sky

Recall that myths are stories of great adventures or unexplainable events that happened long ago. Imagine that you are a story writer, gazing at the night sky. Choose a constellation and give it a new name. Then develop your own myth about how that constellation got its name. Be sure to include names and descriptions of characters. Draw the constellation too.

Assessment – Section 1

1. Use your ruler and pencil to measure and draw a 20-cm (8-in.) line lengthwise down the center of the paper. Make a dot at the midpoint of the line. Label the dot S. Draw a circle with a 5-cm radius whose focus is at S. Label it *Shape A*. What is the circle's diameter?

_____

How did you figure that out?

_____

_____

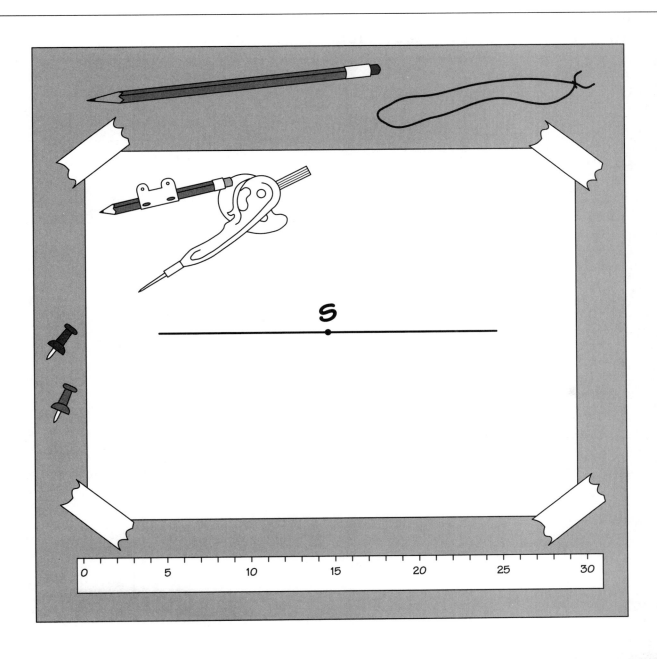

Assessment – Section 1

2. Make two more dots on the line—at the two points where the line and the circle meet. Press push pins into the dots, leaving just enough space so the string can move freely underneath them.

3. Place the string loop around the push pins. Insert the pencil tip into the loop and pull gently so that the string does not droop. What shape do you predict that you will be making if you move the pencil around the two push pins?

_____

4. Keeping gentle pressure on the loop of string, draw a line as you move the pencil around the two push pins. Label the shape your line traces *Shape B.* What shape did you produce?

_____

Was your prediction correct?

_____

In our Solar System, which objects follow this sort of path around the Sun?

_____

What is this path called?

_____

Why isn't the path a perfect circle?

_____

_____

_____

_____

Assessment – Section 2

1. The chart below shows the names of the planets, as well as their actual diameters. Using a scale of 1 cm:10,000 km, calculate the scale model diameters, and enter them in the third column (three are already completed for you).

Name	Actual Diameter (km)	Scale Model Diameter (cm) Scale = 1 cm:10,000 km
Sun	1,392,000	139.2
Mercury	4,878	
Venus	12,100	
Earth	12,756	
Mars	6,786	
Jupiter	143,200	
Saturn	120,536	
Uranus	51,118	5.1
Neptune	49,528	
Pluto	2,400	0.24

Using the zero mark on the ruler below as the focus of your planet circle, draw and label one planet to scale. Draw your planet freehand.

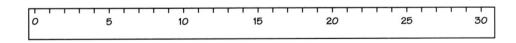

Why are scale models helpful?

_____

_____

_____

_____

Assessment – Section 2

2. A solar system is made up of a star and all the objects that travel around it. Based on this definition, create your own solar system in the space below. Make sure that you label everything you draw, including the paths of the orbits around the star.

3. Draw a sketch or write a paragraph about how the space terms below are related to each other. (Hint—the universe is the largest object.)

     Planet   Galaxy   Star   Universe   Moon

Assessment — Section 3

1. Michael, Juan and Dee Dee stared up at the sky on a clear, moonless night. Suddenly, a white light shot across the sky, with no tail trailing behind. Michael stated that it was a meteor. Juan thought that it was an asteroid and Dee Dee said it was a comet. Who was correct and why?

_____

_____

_____

_____

_____

_____

_____

Dee Dee added that if they looked up at the same spot in three months, the constellations would be in an entirely different part of the sky. Using the term *revolution,* explain why Dee Dee is right.

_____

_____

_____

_____

_____

_____

_____

Assessment – Section 3

2. Anthony wants to build a scale model of his town. What information does he need to know before he starts his project? What must he decide before he lays out his "town"? Use the terms *scale, ratio* and *relative size* in your response.

_____

_____

_____

_____

_____

_____

_____

_____

3. You learned a trick (called a *mnemonic device*) to help remember the names of the planets in order of their distance from the Sun. One of the sentences was "Many Very Energetic Moms Join Some Unique New Programs," which helped you to remember that the nine planets are Mercury, Venus, Earth, Mars, Jupiter, Saturn, Uranus, Neptune, and Pluto. Think of a sentence of your own that will help you remember the planets in their correct order.

_____

_____

_____

_____

_____

A box turtle stretches its neck and smells the air on a sunny day. Another snacks on wild strawberries. In summer, turtles find a lot of berries, worms, and insects to eat.

In the spring or early summer, the female turtle laid eggs in a hole she dug. After covering them with dirt, she left them to hatch later in the summer.

Scram! A female goose flaps her wings and hisses at a skunk that has come near her nest.

The skunk might be a mother trying to take the eggs to feed her own young. Do you think the goose can scare the skunk away?

Baby geese, called goslings, follow their mother into a pond. Like many other baby animals, they grow up in summer. By fall, the goslings will be almost as big as their mother.

One by one, baby box turtles and king snakes wiggle out of their shells. The babies are on their own as soon as they hatch. Their mothers wandered off after laying the eggs.

Only one week old, they can already swim.
The goslings can get their own food, too, but
they still need their mother nearby.

At the edge of a swamp, a mother deer keeps a lookout as her fawn takes a drink of water. The fawn will not leave its mother until next year. For now, it learns how to find food and stay alert for danger by watching what she does.

All day and night in summer, the buzzing and humming of insects fill the air. The polka-dot insects do not sing. They are ladybird beetles, also called ladybugs. They eat other insects such as aphids. Tiny red aphids suck juices from a plant. Some of the aphids have wings.
Can you find the one on this plant that has wings?

A cicada has just shed its "skin." Soon it will harden and look like the cicadas hanging on the leaves. You can hear the loud song of cicadas in summer.

Birds need to catch a lot of insects to feed the young that were hatched in spring. A baby redstart stays snug beside its parent in the nest. The little bird is helpless and cannot open its eyes yet. Its feathers have not all grown in.

A yellow warbler drops an insect into the mouth of one of its young. For days the baby birds will just chirp and eat. But in less than two weeks, they will fly off alone.

Young animals are up in the trees, down in the meadow, just about everywhere late in summer. A gray wolf pup that goes off to play keeps in touch with its mother by howling. This helps her find the pup if an enemy comes near.

As young animals grow older, they begin to explore. A bear cub climbs a pine tree and licks the bark. The cub holds on with its sharp claws. Bear cubs play in the trees. They also go up them to sniff out honey and to escape danger.

Peekaboo! A squirrel hides out in its tree hole. Young raccoons may find shelter in dens on the ground. In the water they catch fish and frogs to eat.

How lazy a bullfrog looks
as it floats on the water.
The frog spends some of its day
on land, waiting to catch insects.
It is still growing. In a few days,
the little tail on top of its back
will disappear.

Turtles living in a pond often
warm their bodies in the sun
during the day. Sometimes they
crawl out on a log. They poke
their heads out and look around.

Wherever there are ponds or streams, you can find animals in summer. A black-and-white warbler hops in the water, then rolls on his side with a splash. The warbler is cleaning his feathers. Maybe he's cooling off. Birds bathe all year long, but they do it more often when the weather is hot and dry.

Animals get thirsty on a hot day. A chipmunk leans over to drink from a quiet stream. You might see a chipmunk at a puddle in the woods after a summer shower.

Whoosh! Thousands of bats leave their cave at sunset to find insects to eat. Another kind of bat uses its long tongue to sip liquid from a flower. In almost the same way, a moth drinks from a zinnia. As the bat and the moth fly from flower to flower, they carry yellow dust, or pollen, on their bodies.

Many animals live in a swamp.
A green-backed heron holds a sunfish in
its bill. The bird returns to the swamp
each summer because it can find insects
and fish to eat. A green tree frog
munches a dragonfly it caught.

With its long bill, a limpkin reaches
into the shell of an apple snail. This
swamp bird eats almost nothing else.

Autumn is finally on the way! The little pika gathers a pile of leaves and stems to store for winter. Squirrels stuff themselves with food. One bites into a mushroom. Another buries nuts.

Summer is a wonderful season for all creatures. As it comes to an end, they work hard to stay warm and well-fed through the winter.

MORE ABOUT Animals in Summer

As the long, hot days of summer arrive, meadows and woodlands are alive with animal activity. Swarms of insects whirl in the air, baby birds chirp, and spiders spin webs. Vacations and outdoor activities such as hiking, fishing, and camping offer families the chance to observe a variety of creatures. For most of the animals, summer is the season for raising young.

Why do we have summer? The seasons change as the earth makes its yearly journey around the sun on a tilted axis. From March 20 to September 23, the northern hemisphere is tipped toward the sun, bringing higher temperatures and longer days to this part of the world. Summer weather is not the same everywhere, however; and along with variations of the weather come differences in animal behavior. Snow melts slowly in the mountains (2-3),* and cold weather lingers. Creatures in the mountains may not emerge from their winter retreats as early as they do elsewhere.

The abundance of food in summer and added hours of daylight for foraging provide favorable conditions for growing up. Egg laying for many species usually occurs in spring, and hatching of the young takes place as the warm weather sets in.

In many areas, box turtles (4-5, 8) hatch from eggs that were buried in the ground by the female in late spring and early summer. When they are ready to hatch about three months later, the baby turtles tear at the eggshells, using an egg tooth. These sharp little projections on their noses eventually fall off. Next, the turtles must make their way out of their underground nest, a process that can

take several days. Once above the ground, the turtles are able to feed themselves and move about, but they are still vulnerable to predators until their outer shells are more developed.

Sharing the woods with box turtles are king snakes (8), which also must fend for themselves as soon as they hatch. In spring the female snake hides her eggs under leaves or logs or in the soil. This protects the embryos and provides them with warmth and moisture. By late summer the snakes are ready to come out of their leathery shells. They, too, tear them open with an egg tooth. The snakes stay in the shells for a few more days, drawing nourishment from the remains of the yolk.

Other young animals rely on their parents for protection and guidance for weeks or longer. Fawns (cover, 10-11), for example, tag along with their mothers for up to two years and learn by copying them.

Birds that are altricial, such as the warbler (14), are blind, featherless, and require constant care at first. With their parents tending them, they develop quickly. They leave the nest within two weeks. Even baby animals that are able to do many things at first need their parents for guidance. Precocial birds, such as geese (8-9), can see, walk, and feed themselves just after hatching. Instinctively, however, they follow their parents, depending on them to lead them to food.

Just as children do, young animals like to explore in the summertime. A wolf pup may wander into a meadow full of flowers (16-17). Bear cubs (18) climb trees with their sharp claws, sometimes in search of bees' honey.

Yellow pollen sticks to a bumblebee's leg as the bee sips nectar from an aster. By carrying pollen from flower to flower, the bee helps plants reproduce.

Animals have ways of coping with summer heat. Some wallow in mud. Others seek shade. Certain animals respond to excessive heat by aestivating, entering a dormant state. One kind of frog burrows underground and sheds a layer of skin, which covers the frog and helps seal in moisture. Other animals, such as warblers (22-23), deal with heat by bathing often. Besides helping them cool off, bathing conditions their feathers by stimulating oil secretion. And it gets rid of parasites.

While some animals avoid heat, others seek it out. Painted turtles (21)—a common aquatic species—

*Numbers in parentheses refer to pages in *Animals in Summer*.

depend on the sun for body heat. Like all reptiles, they are cold-blooded and unable to control their internal temperature. The turtles warm themselves by taking brief sunbaths. As summer wanes and the temperature goes down, the turtles grow sluggish, eventually becoming inactive.

Early in summer tadpoles develop near the water's edge. Most turn rapidly into frogs (27) as they grow lungs and legs. A large bullfrog (20), however, can take more than a year to mature. The deep calls of the bullfrog can often be heard on a summer evening.

The buzzing of insects can be heard day or night. Among the loudest is the cicada (12). The immature cicada grows for years in the ground, protected by a tough exoskeleton. It emerges from the ground, climbs a tree, and sheds its exoskeleton on the trunk. After a brief mating season, the cicada dies in a few weeks.

The female garden spider mates in late summer. She encloses her eggs in a case she spins of silk from her body, and dies soon afterward. The young hatch, then remain quietly in their protective sac in the web until the following spring. In contrast, green lynx spiderlings leave their egg sac before winter and hibernate under bark or a leaf. They spin thin strands of silk, which are easily caught by breezes. The spiderlings may ride the silken strands for some miles.

Spiders benefit from the many insects available in summer, as do tree frogs (27), turtles, birds, and bats (24-25). At twilight bats fly out from their homes in caves and other places to search for insects. Other kinds of bats sip nectar from flowers, spreading pollen at the same time.

The prevalence of food in this season lures birds like the green-

On a June day, a nanny and her kid look down from a high ridge.
The adult mountain goat has shed most of her shaggy winter coat.

backed heron (26) to the same marsh each year. The heron dips into the water to jab small fish with its sharp, pointed beak.

Without summer's bounty, many animals could not survive a harsh winter. Squirrels (19, 28) storing nuts in the ground and in tree holes is a familiar sight as the days begin to shorten. Even earlier, pikas (28-29) scurry across mountainsides, cutting and gathering stems and roots of plants, which they lay in the sun to dry. Pikas build haystacks, often several feet tall, beside their homes in the rocks. During snowstorms a pika just steps out of its home to reach the food.

Whether you go to the mountains or to the seashore, or stay close to home, you'll be sure to discover busy animals in summer. The following activities can guide you and your children in observing the animals in your area. If you live where there are no marked seasonal differences, you may want to compare the cycle of

creatures around you to those in other regions of the country. At what time of year, for example, do you see baby birds hatching?

Select a tree or a space near your home and study the habits of the creatures living there. What do they eat? When do they rest? Do they have young? If so, try to follow their development. *But do not disturb the animals or their homes.*

See how many kinds of insects you can spot, but be careful not to touch them. Some may sting or bite. Record in a notebook what they look like or draw pictures of them. What sounds do they make? Then borrow an insect book from your library to identify them. Look up the differences between insects and spiders.

Choose an animal you like such as a bird or raccoon. Write a story or draw pictures of how it spends its summer. At your library gather books to help you learn more about your creature. What does it do at other times of the year? Does it migrate or hibernate?

If you or a friend have a dog or a cat, you can observe ways animals survive heat in summer. Does the pet pant a lot, move around less, or sit in the shade? Does it drink a lot of water? What do *you* do to stay cool in summer?

A praying mantis rests on a goldenrod plant. This kind of insect lives only one summer. The female lays eggs, then dies in autumn.

COVER: White flowers help hide a fawn as it explores a meadow.

The text by Jane R. McCauley was prepared with input from scientific consultants Eirik A.T. Blom, Maryland Ornithological Society; Dr. Ronald M. Nowak, U.S. Department of the Interior; Dr. Robert O. Petty, Biologist; Louis N. Sorkin, American Museum of Natural History; William A. Xanten, National Zoological Park, Smithsonian Institution. Educational consultant Peter L. Munroe and reading consultant Dr. Lynda Bush also provided helpful comments and suggestions. Original research was provided by Gail N. Hawkins. Prior to paperback publication, the National Geographic Society reviewed the book to ensure its accuracy in light of current information and study.

The photographs were selected by the National Geographic Society's illustrations editor John G. Agnone.
Credits: Len Rue, Jr. (cover); Dwight R. Kuhn (1); John W. Warden (2-3); Joe McDonald (4 upper); Tom Brakefield (4 lower); E.R. Degginger (5, 8 upper, 8 lower, 12 lower right, 13, 19 lower left); Thomas Kitchin (6-7, 28-29); Laura Riley (8-9, 27 lower, 32); James A. Kern (10-11); Robert and Linda Mitchell (12 upper); Bates Littlehales (12 lower left, 22, 23, 26); John Gerlach (14); Jan L. Wassink (15); Jess R. Lee (16-17); Warren Garst / CLICK / Chicago (18); Frederick D. Atwood (19 right); J.A. Wilkinson / VALAN PHOTOS (20 left); John M. Burnley (20-21); Tom J. Ulrich (23 upper); Merlin D. Tuttle / Bat Conservation International (24 lower, 24-25); E.P.I. Nancy Adams (25 lower); Ronny Paille (27 upper); Thomas Kitchin / VALAN PHOTOS (28 upper left); Stephen J. Krasemann / VALAN PHOTOS (28 lower left); Dwight R. Kuhn (30); Art Wolfe (31).

ISBN 0-439-13962-7

12 11 10 9 8 7 6 5 4 3 2 1   9/9 0 1 2 3 4/0

Printed in the U.S.A.   14
First Scholastic printing, November 1999